Letts

GCSE SUCCESS

VISUAL REVISION GUIDE

QUESTIONS & ANSWERS

& ANSWERS

DESIGN & TECHNOLOGY
RESISTANT MATERIALS

Author

Chris Hughes

CONTENTS

HOMEWORK DIARY — 4

EXAM HINTS — 5

MATERIALS AND COMPONENTS

PROPERTIES OF MATERIALS — 6

MATERIAL CHOICE IN DESIGN — 8

MATERIAL FORMS — 10

METALS 1 — 12

METALS 2 — 14

HEAT TREATMENT PROCESSES — 16

PLASTICS — 18

WOODS — 20

COMPOSITE MATERIALS AND SMART MATERIALS — 22

COMPONENTS AND ADHESIVES — 24

DESIGN AND MARKET INFLUENCES

PRODUCT ANALYSIS — 26

GENERATING DESIGN PROPOSALS — 28

PRODUCT DEVELOPMENT AND PLANNING — 30

SOCIAL AND ENVIRONMENTAL CARE — 32

USE OF CAD — 34

SYSTEMS AND CONTROL DESIGN — 36

MANUFACTURING PROCESSES

SAFE WORKING PROCEDURES — 38

PREPARATION FOR MANUFACTURE — 40

HAND TOOLS FOR METALS AND PLASTICS — 42

HAND TOOLS FOR WOOD — 44

MACHINE TOOLS FOR METALS AND PLASTICS — 46

MACHINE TOOLS FOR WOOD — 48

REFORMING METALS — 50

REFORMING PLASTICS — 52

DEFORMING WOOD, METALS AND PLASTICS — 54

PERMANENT JOINTING OF METALS AND PLASTICS — 56

PERMANENT JOINTING OF WOOD — 58

TEMPORARY FASTENING METHODS — 60

KNOCK-DOWN FITTINGS — 62

ASSEMBLY AND FITTING — 64

FINISHING PROCESSES FOR WOOD — 66

FINISHING PROCESSES FOR METAL AND PLASTICS — 68

CNC IN MANUFACTURING — 70

TESTING FOR QUALITY — 72

INDUSTRIAL APPLICATIONS

TYPES OF PRODUCTION — 74

COMMERCIAL SYSTEMS — 76

BATCH PRODUCTION — 78

USE OF STANDARD COMPONENTS — 80

USE OF CAD/CAM IN INDUSTRY — 82

COMPUTER INTEGRATED SYSTEMS — 84

CONTROLLING THE QUALITY — 86

GCSE-STYLE QUESTIONS — 89

HOMEWORK DIARY

TOPIC	SCORE
Properties of Materials	/37
Material Choice in Design	/31
Material Forms	/31
Metals 1	/26
Metals 2	/22
Heat Treatment Processes	/28
Plastics	/41
Woods	/36
Composite Materials and Smart Materials	/32
Components and Adhesives	/31
Product Analysis	/34
Generating Design Proposals	/34
Product Development and Planning	/35
Social and Environmental Care	/31
Use of CAD	/27
Systems and Control Design	/28
Safe Working Procedures	/32
Preparation for Manufacture	/30
Hand Tools for Metals and Plastics	/27
Hand Tools for Wood	/28
Machine Tools for Metals and Plastics	/34
Machine Tools for Wood	/23
Reforming Metals	/35
Reforming Plastics	/30
Deforming Wood, Metals and Plastics	/30
Permanent Jointing of Metals and Plastics	/39
Permanent Jointing of Wood	/33
Temporary Fastening Methods	/34
Knock-Down Fittings	/33
Assembly and Fitting	/29
Finishing Processes for Wood	/29
Finishing Processes for Metal and Plastics	/31
CNC in Manufacturing	/32
Testing for Quality	/26
Types of Production	/34
Commercial Systems	/28
Batch Production	/36
Use of Standard Components	/31
Use of CAD/CAM in Industry	/34
Computer Integrated Systems	/26
Controlling the Quality	/28

EXAM HINTS

Many GCSE questions will start off with an example of a product or situation to be analysed. This is the context of the question. Always look at the diagrams carefully and read the rest of the question. This will help ensure that you understand the focus of the question. Questions are likely to be divided into a number of inter-related sections that lead you through the steps that the examiner wants you to answer. For example, a question might focus on the type of material used for a product, the reason the material is used and how the material might affect the product specification and use. When answering questions always try and use a neat sketch or diagram. Label it clearly and try and use the correct terminology. Remember to consider environmental and other factors in your answers.

Here are ten tips to help make revision easier and the examinations more stress-free.

- KNOW YOUR COURSE – Make a topic checklist by going through your GCSE specification or by asking your teacher.

- MAKE A REVISION TIMETABLE – Draw up a plan covering all the topics and set a realistic number of hours for revision each week. Note the dates and times of your exams and leave a week or two before each exam for final revision.

- REVISE EFFECTIVELY – Short bursts of about 30 minutes followed by a break work best. Make your revision active – summarise your notes, highlight key points, draw diagrams, use stick-on notes, record yourself on cassette, ask someone to test you.

- BOOST YOUR MEMORY – Find the way of learning that suits you best. Try breaking down the topics into chunks and use key words, images, mnemonics, rhymes and colour-coding to trigger your memory.

- PRACTISE QUESTIONS – Get used to the style of questions used in the exams. Highlight the key words in the question, plan your response and ensure that your answer is relevant.

- THINK POSITIVE – Look back at your original plan from time to time, and realise the progress you have made. If there are areas that you find particularly difficult, ask your teacher for help.

- HANDLING STRESS – Start preparing for the exams early. Take breaks from revising, exercise regularly, eat and sleep well. Remind yourself that it will all be over in a couple of months!

- THE WEEK BEFORE – Allow time for final revision when you can go over essential or difficult points.

- THE NIGHT BEFORE – Look over a few points but don't try to cram lots of new information. Get all your equipment ready – pens, pencils, calculator, ruler, etc. Have an early night.

- IN THE EXAM – Follow all the instructions on the exam paper. Read the questions carefully and ensure you answer the question asked. Check the number of marks available for each question and answer accordingly. Keep an eye on the time – make sure you answer the correct number of questions and leave time to read through your answers.

We hope you find this book useful in preparing for your exams. Good Luck!

PROPERTIES OF MATERIALS

A Choose just one answer, a, b, c or d.

1 Hardness is an example of:
a) a physical property
b) an aesthetic property
c) a mechanical property
d) a force property   (1 mark)

2 Tensile strength is the ability of a material to withstand:
a) pushing forces
b) pulling forces
c) bending forces
d) twisting forces   (1 mark)

3 Brittle materials have low resistance to:
a) impact loads
b) corrosion
c) electrical conductivity
d) indentation and scratching   (1 mark)

4 Bending strength is an important consideration for:
a) fishing rods
b) centre punches
c) rock-climbing ropes
d) table tops   (1 mark)

5 The properties of a material can be described as:
a) the cost of the material
b) the surface of the material
c) the characteristics of the material
d) the structure of the material   (1 mark)

Score   / 5

B Answer all parts of the questions.

1 Decide whether these statements are true or false.

	True	False
a) Torsional strength is the ability to withstand twisting forces.	☐	☐
b) Hardness is an important property for twist drills.	☐	☐
c) Elasticity is a measure of how brittle a material is.	☐	☐
d) Thermal conductivity is a measure of how well a material can conduct heat.	☐	☐
e) Electrical insulators are materials which allow electricity to flow through them easily.	☐	☐ (5 marks)

2 Complete these sentences using one of the following words.

ductile	cold-worked	malleability	machineability

a) .... is an important property when turning metals on a lathe.

b) When hammering a piece of aluminium it hardens due to being ....

c) When wire is manufactured by pulling it through a die it needs to be ....

d) .... is the ability of a material to be hammered or forged into shape.

(4 marks)

Score   / 9

These are GCSE-style questions. Answer all parts of the questions.

1 a) State what is meant by the term 'property' of a material.

....

....

....

....
(2 marks)

conducting
pins

the body

insulation for
the wires

wires

b) For the three-pin plug, state a material which could be used for:

i) the body .... (2 marks)

ii) the conducting pins .... (1 mark)

iii) the conducting wires .... (1 mark)

iv) the insulation on the wires .... (2 marks)

c) For each of the materials state two properties which make them suitable for the product.

Part	Two Properties	
Body		
Conducting pins		
Conducting wires		
Insulation on the wires		

(8 marks)

2 a) The table below lists a number of sports products. A property that is common to each of them is toughness. Complete the table with two other properties that are required when the products are being used.

Product	Properties	
Pole-vaulting pole		
Rock-climbing rope		
Hockey stick		
Running shoes		
Tennis racket frame		

(5 marks)

b) Why is toughness an important property for these products?

....

....
(2 marks)

Score   / 23

How well did you do?

0–10 correct   Try again
11–19 correct   Getting there
20–31 correct   Good work
32–37 correct   Excellent!

TOTAL SCORE   / 37

For more information on this topic
see pages 4–5 of your Success Guide

MATERIAL CHOICE IN DESIGN

A | **Choose just one answer, a, b, c or d.**

1 Plates, tubes, squares and round bars are all:
a) examples of standard metals
b) ironmonger's sections
c) standard sections
d) material parts   (1 mark)

2 A biodegradable material is one that will:
a) naturally degrade in the environment
b) grow naturally in the environment
c) not grow naturally in the environment
d) form natural shapes when left in the environment   (1 mark)

3 The term service property relates specifically to:
a) how the product will be manufactured
b) how the product will be costed
c) the intended use of the product
d) economic factors   (1 mark)

4 Good resistance to corrosion is generally regarded as:
a) a manufacturing property
b) an economic property
c) a general property
d) a service property   (1 mark)

5 Manufacturing properties are required so that the product:
a) can be made with the available equipment
b) can be made to the correct size
c) can be costed correctly
d) works well when being used   (1 mark)

Score   / 5

B | **Answer all parts of the question.**

1 The child's tricycle shown is to be manufactured in a plastics material.

a) State two service properties for the tricycle.

....

....   (2 marks)

b) Give two manufacturing properties that would need to be considered.

....

....   (2 marks)

c) Explain why it might be cheaper to produce the product in plastics rather than in metals.

....

....

....

....   (4 marks)

Score / 8

C These are GCSE-style questions. Answer all parts of the questions.

1 Thirty wooden toy trains are to be made in your workshop.

   a) Make a list of five costs that would have to be taken into account when making the toy.

   ....

   ....

   ....

   ....

   .... (5 marks)

   b) Give two environmental factors that you would have to consider when ordering materials for making the train.

   ....

   .... (2 marks)

   c) Why would standard sections be suitable for many parts of this product?

   ....

   ....

   .... (3 marks)

2 A set of ten rocking-horses is to be designed and made in a school workshop.

   a) Give three service requirements for each product.

   ....

   ....

   .... (3 marks)

   b) What manufacturing factors would you have to consider before making the product?

   ....

   ....

   .... (3 marks)

   c) Give two other factors you would consider during the design and making stages.

   ....

   .... (2 marks)

   Score   / 18

How well did you do?

0–8 correct   Try again
9–17 correct   Getting there
18–23 correct   Good work
24–31 correct   Excellent!

TOTAL SCORE   / 31

For more information on this topic
see pages 6–7 of your Success Guide

MATERIAL FORMS

A

Choose just one answer, a, b, c or d.

1 Which of the following is not a semi-finished steel-making process product?
a) billet
b) bloom
c) bus
d) slab
(1 mark)

2 Black mild steel is often used for:
a) decorative forge work
b) machine parts
c) car axles
d) metal working vices
(1 mark)

3 When turning down a square-sectioned bar on a centre lathe it is normally held in a:
a) three-jaw chuck
b) four-jaw chuck
c) drill chuck
d) face plate
(1 mark)

4 BDMS stands for:
a) black drawn medium steel
b) bright dimensional machined steel
c) black dense metal section
d) bright drawn mild steel
(1 mark)

5 The material used for vacuum forming plastics comes in the form of:
a) thin plastic film
b) hexagonal bar
c) plastic granules
d) thin sheet
(1 mark)

Score / 5

B

Answer all parts of the questions.

Choose one of these phrases to fill in each gap in the sentences below.

| manufacturers' catalogues | volume | cross-sections |
| accurate finish | lathe chuck | standard stock sizes |

1 Materials are available in a number of ....

2 .... give the range of standard sizes available.

3 Hardwoods tend to be sold by ....

4 Metals are available in a number of different ....

5 Bright drawn mild steel has been drawn through a die to give an ....

6 Bright drawn mild steel can be used directly in a .... (6 marks)

Score / 6

C | These are GCSE-style questions. Answer all parts of the questions.

1 You have been asked to make the axle for a child's toy. The axle is shown in the diagram.

spacer — *nut*
metal axle
nut — *spacer*
axle

a) What type of metal sectional bar could you use for the axle and the wheel spacers?

.... (1 mark)

b) Give two reasons why you have chosen these types of sections.

Reason 1 ....

Reason 2 .... (2 marks)

c) Describe the process you would use to make the thread at the end of the bar.

....

....

.... (4 marks)

d) Describe how you could make the spacers.

....

....

.... (4 marks)

2 You have been asked to order a range of stock materials for a school workshop.

a) For each application state what material form you would order.

Application	Material Form
Vacuum-formed boxes	
Plastic labels to stick onto the boxes	
Material to make reinforced plastic products	
Material for injection moulding machine	
Metal for decorative forge work	
12 mm bar for general lathe work	
Wood for making toy car axles	

(7 marks)

b) Explain the advantage of using bright drawn mild steel for machining applications in the workshop.

....

.... (2 marks)

Score   / 20

How well did you do?

0–8 correct	Try again
9–17 correct	Getting there
18–23 correct	Good work
24–31 correct	Excellent!

TOTAL SCORE   /31

For more information on this topic see pages 8–9 of your Success Guide

METALS 1

A

Choose just one answer, a, b, c or d.

1 Which of the following materials is a ferrous metal?
a) copper
b) aluminium
c) mild steel
d) lead   (1 mark)

2 A medium carbon steel has a carbon content of:
a) 2%–5%
b) 0.35%–0.7%
c) 10%–15%
d) 20%–30%   (1 mark)

3 Plain carbon steels are alloys of:
a) aluminium and carbon
b) aluminium and oxygen
c) iron and oxygen
d) iron and carbon   (1 mark)

4 Soft solder is an alloy of:
a) copper and zinc
b) tin and lead
c) aluminium and lead
d) iron and lead   (1 mark)

5 Which of the following metals will need protecting against rusting when being used outside?
a) bronze
b) duralumin
c) stainless steel
d) mild steel   (1 mark)

Score   / 5

B

Answer all parts of the questions.

1 Choose one of the following words to complete each of these sentences.

| type | stronger | physical | pure |

a) Alloys are mixtures of two or more .... metals.

b) Pure metals contain only one .... of metal.

c) Alloys tend to be .... than pure metals.

d) Alloys tend to have better .... properties than pure metals.

(4 marks)

2 State what effect increasing the carbon content of a steel has on its hardness, toughness and ductility.

....

....

....

(2 marks)

Score   /6

C These are GCSE-style questions. Answer all parts of the questions.

1 a) The table gives some uses of metals that are used in design and technology applications. Complete the table giving the type of metal that is commonly used in each case. The first example has been done for you.

Use	Metal
Food cans	tin plate
Metal work vices	
Drill bits for wood	
Kitchen sinks	
The pins of a 13-amp plug	
The wire in electrical cables	

(5 marks)

b) Give two reasons why kitchen saucepans are often made from aluminium.

....

.... (2 marks)

c) Mild steel is often used for making products for outside use.

Give two methods that can be used to protect the metal when it is being used outside.

....

.... (2 marks)

2 Copper is a commonly used metal for central heating pipes.

a) Give two reasons why it is a suitable material for this application.

....

.... (2 marks)

b) Give one other example of a copper-based alloy that could be used for some of the central heating fittings.

.... (1 mark)

c) What alloy would be used to join the pipe and fittings together?

.... (1 mark)

d) What is the composition of this alloy?

....

.... (2 marks)

Score   / 15

How well did you do?

0–6 correct	Try again
7–12 correct	Getting there
13–20 correct	Good work
21–26 correct	Excellent!

TOTAL SCORE   / 26

For more information on this topic see pages 10–11 of your Success Guide

METALS 2

A

Choose just one answer, a, b, c or d.

1 Ferrous metals are those that contain:
a) brass
b) aluminium
c) iron
d) lead   (1 mark)

2 Tin is an example of a:
a) non-ferrous metal
b) ferrous metal
c) tool steel
d) malleable steel   (1 mark)

3 Cast irons have around:
a) 3.5%–4.0% carbon
b) 0.1%–0.2% carbon
c) 0.01%–0.02% carbon
d) 1%–2% carbon   (1 mark)

4 Stainless steels contain:
a) aluminium
b) bronze
c) solder
d) chromium   (1 mark)

5 Brass is an alloy of:
a) copper and zinc
b) copper and aluminium
c) zinc and lead
d) tin and aluminium   (1 mark)

Score   / 5

B

Answer all parts of the questions.

1 Match these carbon contents to the metals shown in the table.

| 0.35%–0.7% carbon | 3.5%–4.5% carbon | 0.8%–1.5% carbon | 0.15%–0.35% carbon |

Metal	Carbon Content
Cast iron	
High carbon steel	
Mild steel	
Medium carbon steel	

(4 marks)

2 The table shows a range of common metals. What are the constituents of the metals? The first one has been completed for you.

Material	Composition
Mild steel	iron and carbon
Bronze	
Duralumin	
Solder	
Stainless steel	

(4 marks)

Score   / 8

C This is a GCSE-style question. Answer all parts of the question.

1 The diagram below shows the design of a household kettle.
It could be manufactured from either metal or plastics.

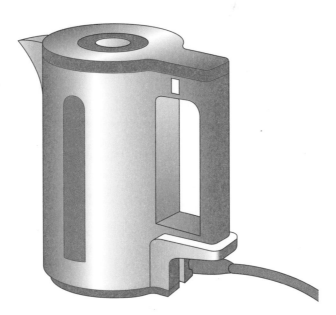

a) Name a metal material that could be used to make the kettle.

.... (1 mark)

b) Name a plastics material that could be used to make the kettle.

.... (1 mark)

c) Give three service properties that are required when it is being used.

....

....

.... (3 marks)

d) State two advantages of using a metal rather than a plastics material in its manufacture.

....

.... (2 marks)

e) State two disadvantages of using a metal rather than using a plastic.

....

.... (2 marks)

Score   / 9

How well did you do?

0–6 correct   Try again
7–12 correct   Getting there
13–18 correct   Good work
19–22 correct   Excellent!

TOTAL SCORE   / 22

For more information on this topic
see pages 10–11 of your Success Guide

HEAT TREATMENT PROCESSES

A Choose just one answer, a, b, c or d.

1 Hardening and tempering of plain carbon steels can only be carried out on steels that have a carbon content greater than about:
a) 0.2% b) 0.4%
c) 0.01% d) 0.02% (1 mark)

2 Mild steel can be hardened by:
a) case hardening
b) quenching in oil
c) centre hardening
d) normalising (1 mark)

3 When a cold metal is hammered heavily it will:
a) melt b) case harden
c) work harden d) centre harden (1 mark)

4 Which of the following products would be hardened and tempered to improve its properties?
a) hacksaw blade
b) car body
c) metal teapot
d) chicken wire (1 mark)

5 Heat treatment processes are generally used to improve the properties of:
a) wood
b) plastics
c) metals
d) paper (1 mark)

Score /5

B Answer all parts of the questions.

1 Consider the following statements. State whether they are true or false.   True   False

a) Annealing is a heat treatment process used to soften a metal when it has become work hardened. ☐ ☐

b) Hardening and tempering of steels is used to increase the hardness of products such as hammers and centre punches. ☐ ☐

c) Normalising is used to improve the strength and toughness of steel products after forging or rolling. ☐ ☐

d) Case hardening is used on aluminium and brass to improve appearance. ☐ ☐ (4 marks)

2 Rearrange the following sentences to explain why annealing may be required for certain processes in the school workshop.

Annealing softens the metal so that further hammering can take place.

When a metal is hammered it will tend to become harder.

It will eventually become so hard that further hammering cannot be done.

As the metal becomes harder it becomes more difficult to work.

....

....

....

....

(4 marks)
Score / 8

16

C **These are GCSE-style questions. Answer all parts of the questions.**

1 A small coat hook has to be made out of aluminium to the design shown.

5 mm thickness

made from
bent aluminium

a) Briefly explain why aluminium may require annealing before it is bent.

....

....

.... (3 marks)

b) State a simple method that could be used to determine the correct annealing temperature
if the aluminium was being heated up using a brazing torch.

....

.... (2 marks)

c) What will happen if the aluminium is heated up to a far greater temperature than
the annealing temperature?

.... (1 mark)

d) Give two safety precautions that need to be observed when annealing using a
school brazing hearth.

....

.... (2 marks)

2 A cold chisel has been made by shaping a piece of hexagonal steel on a school forge.
The next stage is to harden and temper the cutting edge.

a) What type of metal would be suitable for making the chisel?

.... (1 mark)

b) Explain how the hardening and tempering process could be carried out.

....

....

....

.... (4 marks)

c) What is the purpose of tempering the point once it has been hardened?

....

.... (2 marks)

Score   / 15

How well did you do?

0–8 correct   Try again
9–14 correct   Getting there
15–22 correct Good work
23–28 correct Excellent!

TOTAL SCORE   /28

For more information on this topic
see pages 12–13 of your Success Guide

PLATICS

PLASTICS

A Choose just one answer, a, b, c or d.

1 Which of these describes a plastics material that can be re-shaped when it is re-heated?
a) bent setting plastics
b) thermosetting plastics
c) re-shaping plastics
d) thermoplastics (1 mark)

2 The main 'backbone' of plastic molecules is made up of:
a) oxygen atoms　　b) iron atoms
c) chromium atoms　d) carbon atoms (1 mark)

3 A thermosetting plastic is cured to:
a) introduce colour to the material
b) soften the plastics
c) produce cross-links during the manufacturing stage
d) increase its thickness (1 mark)

4 Thermoplastics are generally manufactured using:
a) compression moulding
b) pressure die casting
c) centre lathe turning
d) injection moulding (1 mark)

5 Which of the following is a thermosetting plastic?
a) nylon
b) PTFE
c) polystyrene
d) melamine formaldehyde (1 mark)

Score　/ 5

B Answer all parts of the questions.

1 Indicate whether the following processes are for thermoplastics or thermosetting plastics.

Process	Type of Plastic
Plastic extrusion	
Transfer moulding	
Vacuum forming	
Compression moulding	
Blow moulding	
Injection moulding	

(6 marks)

2 For each of the plastics below state whether it is a thermoplastic or thermosetting plastic and give two uses for each material. (18 marks)

Plastic	Type	Two Uses
Polystyrene		
Urea formaldehyde		
Melamine formaldehyde		
Polyethylene		
Polyvinyl chloride (PVC)		
Nylon		

Score　/ 24

C **These are GCSE-style questions. Answer all parts of the questions.**

1 A batch of 10 000 picnic boxes is to be made using a type of plastics material.

a) State whether you would use a thermoplastic or thermosetting plastic.

.... (1 mark)

b) Name a plastic that could be used for the boxes.

.... (1 mark)

c) Give four reasons why you have chosen this plastic material for making the boxes.

Reason 1 ....

Reason 2 ....

Reason 3 ....

Reason 4 .... (4 marks)

2 Urea formaldehyde is commonly used for the manufacture of electrical plugs and fittings.

a) Give two properties of the plastic that make it suitable for these applications.

....

.... (2 marks)

b) Name a manufacturing process that could be used to make the products.

.... (1 mark)

c) Explain how curing will alter the properties of the plastic.

....

....

.... (3 marks)

Score   / 12

How well did you do?

0–15 correct   Try again
16–27 correct   Getting there
28–35 correct   Good work
36–41 correct   Excellent!

TOTAL SCORE   / 41

For more information on this topic
see pages 14–15 of your Success Guide

WOODS

A Choose just one answer, a, b, c or d.

1 Softwoods generally come from:
a) broad-leaf (deciduous) trees
b) oak trees
c) beech trees
d) coniferous trees (1 mark)

2 Hardwoods generally come from:
a) scots pine trees
b) coniferous trees
c) broad-leaf (deciduous) trees
d) spruce trees (1 mark)

3 MDF stands for:
a) mild density fibreboard
b) medium density fir
c) mild density fir
d) medium density fibreboard (1 mark)

4 A thinly cut or sliced piece of timber often used to enhance the appearance of manufactured boards is called a:
a) layer
b) veneer
c) sliver
d) shim (1 mark)

5 Which of the following is not a hardwood?
a) balsa wood
b) scots pine
c) ash
d) mahogany (1 mark)

Score / 5

B Answer all parts of the questions.

1 The table below shows some common types of timbers. Complete the table stating whether each timber is a softwood or a hardwood. Give a typical use for each type of wood.

Timber	Softwood or Hardwood	Use
Ash		
Beech		
Oak		
Spruce		

(8 marks)

2 Briefly explain why making wooden products out of softwoods rather than hardwoods is generally better for the environment.

....

....

.... (2 marks)

3 Give three examples of manufactured boards.

Example 1 ....

Example 2 ....

Example 3 .... (3 marks)

Score / 13

C These are GCSE-style questions. Answer all parts of the questions.

1 You have been asked to decide whether to use a manufactured timber or a natural timber when making the doors for the kitchen units shown.

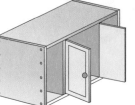

a) Give three advantages of using manufactured boards rather than natural timbers.

Advantage 1 ....

Advantage 2 ....

Advantage 3 .... (3 marks)

b) State two reasons why a natural timber might be preferred.

Reason 1 ....

Reason 2 .... (2 marks)

c) Name two types of rotting or fungal diseases that can occur when natural timbers are used.

....

.... (2 marks)

d) Give two ways in which a natural timber can be protected from such diseases.

....

.... (2 marks)

2 You have been asked to make a range of chairs for your school garden.

a) Name one type of hardwood and one type of softwood that could be used for the job.

....

.... (2 marks)

b) Name some of the defects that you might come across when selecting the wood for the chairs.

....

....

.... (3 marks)

c) What are the causes of wet rot? How might this be avoided when using the chairs outdoors?

....

....

....

.... (4 marks)

Score   / 18

How well did you do?

0–12 correct   Try again
13–21 correct   Getting there
22–29 correct   Good work
30–36 correct   Excellent!

TOTAL SCORE   / 36

For more information on this topic
see pages 16–17 of your Success Guide

COMPOSITE MATERIALS AND SMART MATERIALS

A Choose just one answer, a, b, c or d.

1 Which of the following is not a type of fibre generally used in composite materials?
   a) carbon fibre   b) glass fibre
   c) wood fibre   d) kevlar   (1 mark)

2 A composite material constructed with a lightweight core material glued between two thinner skins is called a:
   a) sandwich beam composite
   b) triple deck composite
   c) fibre composite
   d) tensile composite   (1 mark)

3 Filament winding is often used to make composite:
   a) aircraft wings   b) ships' hulls
   c) car bumpers   d) chemical pipes (1 mark)

4 Smart materials are very often used in:
   a) electrical sensors
   b) table legs
   c) car bodies
   d) garden tools   (1 mark)

5 Which of the following is not a common type of reinforcement construction?
   a) chopped strand mat
   b) woven mat
   c) uniaxial fibre
   d) hexagonal mat   (1 mark)

Score   / 5

B Answer all parts of the questions.

1 Give four typical uses of composite materials.

   Use 1 ....

   Use 2 ....

   Use 3 ....

   Use 4 ....   (4 marks)

2 Decide whether each of the following statements is true or false.

	True	False
a) Composites are now widely used as replacements for metals and plastic components.	☐	☐
b) Fibre composites consist of weak fibres embedded in a much stronger matrix material.	☐	☐
c) Smart materials are materials whose properties can change due to changes in pressure, force or temperature.	☐	☐
d) The poor tensile properties of fibres such as Kevlar reduces the stiffness of a composite material.	☐	☐
e) Sandwich beam constructions are used for many transport applications because they are lightweight.	☐	☐

(5 marks)

Score   / 9

These are GCSE-style questions. Answer all parts of the questions.

1 The diagram shows a small boat hull that is to be made using composite materials.

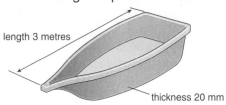

length 3 metres

thickness 20 mm

a) Use a neat sketch to describe how the hull could be made.

(6 marks)

b) State two advantages of using your method rather than by making the hull using traditional materials such as wood.

Advantage 1 ....

Advantage 2 .... (2 marks)

c) What materials would you use in the construction?

....

.... (2 marks)

2 Composite materials are now widely used for piping in the chemical industry.

a) Give three advantages of using composites for pipes rather than metals.

....

....

.... (3 marks)

b) Give an example of a type of composite materials that could be used for making the pipes.

.... (1 mark)

c) What type of manufacturing method is often used to wind the material onto a pipe-shaped former?

.... (1 mark)

d) What are the advantages of making the pipes by machines rather than by hand lay-up methods?

....

....

.... (3 marks)

Score   / 18

How well did you do?

0–9 correct   Try again
10–18 correct   Getting there
19–24 correct   Good work
25–32 correct   Excellent!

TOTAL SCORE   / 32

For more information on this topic
see pages 18–19 of your Success Guide

COMPONENTS AND ADHESIVES

A Choose just one answer, a, b, c or d.

1 Coach bolts are often used for attaching metal parts to:
a) metal frames
b) plastic parts
c) ceramic components
d) wooden frames   (1 mark)

2 Screws that cut their own thread when screwed into a metal or plastic are called:
a) hardening screws
b) engineering screws
c) self-tapping screws
d) cutting screws   (1 mark)

3 Internal screw threads are cut using:
a) dies   b) stocks
c) reamers   d) taps   (1 mark)

4 External screw threads are cut using:
a) files
b) dies
c) taps
d) reamers   (1 mark)

5 Pop rivets are often used to join:
a) sheet metal parts
b) wooden panels
c) mica boards
d) 20 mm-thick cast iron sheets   (1 mark)

Score   / 5

B Answer all parts of the questions.

1 The table lists some of the common types of adhesives used in design and technology. Give one use for each type of adhesive.   (4 marks)

Type of Adhesive	Use
Polyvinyl acetate (PVA)	
Cascamite	
Araldite	
Tensol (acrylic cement)	

2 The diagrams below show a selection of common locking devices. Give the correct label for each type of device.

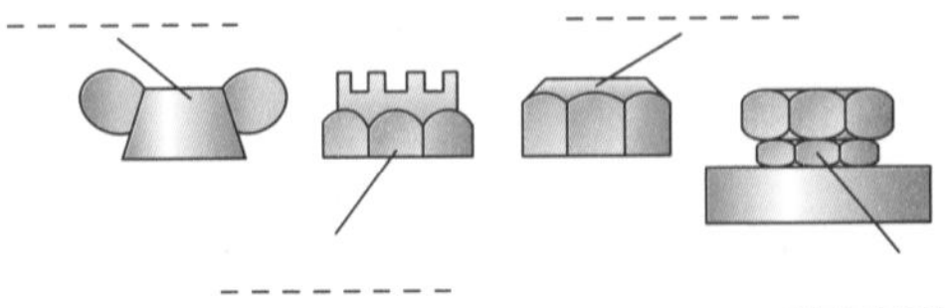

(4 marks)

3 When gluing together metal, plastic or wooden parts it is important to take certain precautions to ensure that you make a quality joint. List three points you would observe when using adhesives for a particular task.

Point 1 ....

Point 2 ....

Point 3 ....

(3 marks)

Score   / 11

C These are GCSE-style questions. Answer all parts of the questions.

1 The shopping trolley shown here is in the process of being designed. One problem is that the wheels need securing to the axle so that they do not become loose when being used.

wheels need to be secured

axle

a) State whether you would use a permanent or temporary fastening to secure the wheels.

.... (1 mark)

b) Give two reasons why you have chosen the particular method to secure the wheels to the axle.

Reason 1 ....

Reason 2 .... (2 marks)

c) Sketch the type of fixing method you would use and add notes to explain why it would not become loose during use.

(6 marks)

2 a) Explain how self-tapping screws are used to join sheet materials together.

....

.... (2 marks)

b) What is the purpose of a washer when used between the head of a nut or bolt and product surface?

....

.... (2 marks)

c) Explain the difference between a set screw and a bolt.

....

.... (2 marks)

Score   / 15

How well did you do?

0–8 correct	Try again
9–17 correct	Getting there
18–23 correct	Good work
24–31 correct	Excellent!

TOTAL SCORE / 31

For more information on this topic see pages 20–21 of your Success Guide

PRODUCT ANALYSIS

A

Choose just one answer, a, b, c or d.

1 **Most products are manufactured:**
a) in batches
b) as one-offs
c) as continuous flow materials
d) using metal castings   (1 mark)

2 **A technique for studying existing products to gather design ideas is often called:**
a) product manufacture
b) tool analysis
c) product analysis
d) study analysis   (1 mark)

3 **Product analysis is generally used in the:**
a) distribution stage
b) quality assessment stage
c) manufacturing stage
d) design and development stage   (1 mark)

4 **Which of the following products would not lend itself to product analysis for school projects?**
a) electrical kettle
b) hairdryer
c) chemical plant
d) mobile phone   (1 mark)

5 **Taking a product apart to help analyse the various parts and how it fits together is called:**
a) commercial analysis
b) safety analysis
c) product disassembly
d) detection analysis   (1 mark)

Score   / 5

B

Answer all parts of the questions.

1 As part of your design studies you have been asked to analyse the design of a hairdryer.

For each of the headings given in the spider diagram, list two factors you would look for in your analysis.

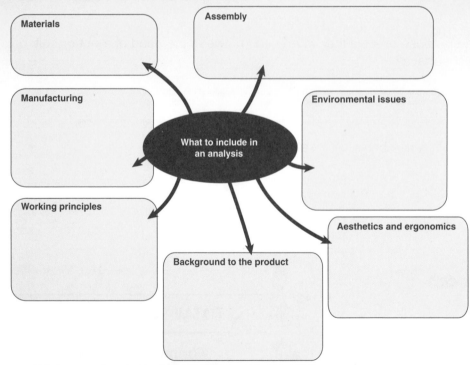

Materials

Assembly

Manufacturing

Environmental issues

What to include in an analysis

Working principles

Aesthetics and ergonomics

Background to the product

(12 marks)

Score   / 12

C **These are GCSE-style questions. Answer all parts of the questions.**

1 The sketch shows a wheelbarrow commonly used in household gardens.

a) Make a checklist under the following headings of some of the points you would look for when carrying out a product analysis.

i) materials

ii) environmental factors

iii) assembly

....

....

....

....

....

.... (6 marks)

b) Select two other products that could be used for a product analysis. Explain why you have chosen them.

Product 1 ....

....

Product 2 ....

.... (4 marks)

2 a) Why might product disassembly be a good method for analysing existing products?

....

.... (3 marks)

b) Make a checklist of factors you might look for during such a disassembly.

....

....

....

.... (4 marks)

Score   / 17

How well did you do?

0–10 correct Try again
11–19 correct Getting there
20–27 correct Good work
28–34 correct Excellent!

TOTAL SCORE   / 34

For more information on this topic
see pages 24–25 of your Success Guide

GENERATING DESIGN PROPOSALS

A

Choose just one answer, a, b, c or d.

1 Design changes that are the result of changes in people's tastes are commonly called:
a) planned obsolescence
b) design changes
c) fashion changes
d) human changes   (1 mark)

2 Adding design features to make a product outdated after a certain time is called:
a) technology obsolescence
b) breakdown obsolescence
c) safety obsolescence
d) planned obsolescence   (1 mark)

3 Developing a design proposal is:
a) the last stage of a design and technology project
b) the first stage of a project
c) not necessary in a project
d) better if carried out in the manufacturing stage of the project   (1 mark)

4 A specific statement of the design problem to be solved is termed the:
a) design essay   b) design factors
c) design brief   d) design list   (1 mark)

5 A chosen area of study from which a design project may be found is called the:
a) design specification
b) design context
c) design list
d) design factors   (1 mark)

Score   / 5

B

Answer all parts of the questions.

1 Consider this list of tasks which refers to stages in the generation of a design proposal. Rearrange the list into the most appropriate order for design development generation.

Define the project need

Carry out research to help in the initial design stages

Prepare a design brief

Write a specification for the project

Choose an area of study (context) from which a project need can be found

Select the best idea or ideas for further development. Give reasons for choices.

....

....

....

....   (6 marks)

2 Give four reasons why design ideas are continually being generated in industries and other areas.

Reason 1 ....

Reason 2 ....

Reason 3 ....

Reason 4 ....   (4 marks)

Score   / 10

These are GCSE-style questions. Answer all parts of the questions.

1 A common piece of outdoor furniture is shown in the diagram. As part of a design and technology project you have been asked to complete the following.

a) State four factors that could be included in the design specification for the product.

....

....

....

.... (4 marks)

b) Outline three factors that could influence the manufacturing route and processes for the product.

....

....

.... (3 marks)

c) Briefly explain why modelling is a useful method in the design proposal stage.

....

.... (2 marks)

2 Mobile phone companies need to constantly update the styles of hand phones.

a) Give three reasons why a company might have to do this.

....

....

.... (3 marks)

b) Give four specification factors that a mobile phone designer might need to consider when designing a new phone for the market.

....

....

....

.... (4 marks)

c) What sort of research could be carried out in order to gather information for a new design?

....

.... (3 marks)

Score   /19

How well did you do?

0–10 correct	Try again
11–19 correct	Getting there
20–27 correct	Good work
28–34 correct	Excellent!

TOTAL SCORE   / 34

For more information on this topic see pages 26–27 of your Success Guide

PRODUCT DEVELOPMENT AND PLANNING

A Choose just one answer, a, b, c or d.

1 Dimensioned drawings that are used for manufacturing are called:
a) initial sketches   b) planning sketches
c) mock-up drawings d) working drawings
(1 mark)

2 Factors that relate the dimensions of people to a product are called:
a) ergonomic factors   b) specification factors
c) population factors   d) aesthetic factors
(1 mark)

3 Aesthetics is concerned with the:
a) weight of a product
b) machineability of a product
c) appearance of a product
d) size of a product   (1 mark)

4 A network chart is a type of:
a) planning chart
b) mock-up chart
c) manufacturing system
d) dimensional drawing   (1 mark)

5 Final working drawings are often produced with the aid of:
a) CNC
b) CAD
c) CAM
d) ROM   (1 mark)

Score   / 5

B Answer all parts of the questions.

1 Complete the sentences below. Use one of the following phrases in each sentence.

| manufacturing route | sketches | final working drawing | final design proposal |

Planning is essential to plan the .... ,

the manufacturing times and how the quality of the product will be controlled.

Computer aided design is widely used to produce the ....

Development makes use of ...., further research

and mock-ups to refine ideas.

During the product development stage, work is carried out to transform the

.... into working drawings.   (4 marks)

2 Give three reasons why accurate mock-up models are useful in the product development and planning stage of the design and manufacture process.

Reason 1 ....

Reason 2 ....

Reason 3 ....   (3 marks)

3 Make a checklist of points you would consider during the design and development stage.

....

....   (4 marks)

Score   / 11

These are GCSE-style questions. Answer all parts of the questions.

1 A cassette rack is to be made using a CNC routing machine and then hand-assembling the machined parts together.

a) Assuming you are starting from the wood-cutting stage, make a list of the procedures that have to be carried out to make the cassette rack.

....

....

....

.... (4 marks)

b) Draw a network, or similar, diagram to show how the stages of manufacture would be linked together during the manufacturing cycle.

(5 marks)

c) Give two other factors that would have to be considered when the product is being manufactured.

....

.... (2 marks)

2 a) What is meant by the term 'design aesthetics'?

....

.... (2 marks)

b) What is meant by the term 'ergonomics'?

....

.... (2 marks)

c) Explain why planning is an important aspect of the design and technology process.

....

....

....

.... (4 marks)

Score   / 19

How well did you do?

0–11 correct	Try again
12–20 correct	Getting there
21–28 correct	Good work
29–35 correct	Excellent!

TOTAL SCORE   / 35

For more information on this topic see pages 28–29 of your Success Guide

SOCIAL AND ENVIRONMENTAL CARE

A

Choose just one answer, a, b, c or d.

1 Chemicals that can cause harm to people and animals are called:
a) chemi products
b) taxic products
c) toxic products
d) bio products   (1 mark)

2 Which of the following is not a renewable energy resource?
a) wind   b) water
c) coal   d) solar power   (1 mark)

3 Manufactured boards are mainly made from:
a) reprocessed newspaper
b) recycled timber
c) new trees that have been felled
d) a combination of plastics
   and timber   (1 mark)

4 Which of the following materials is the most difficult to recycle?
a) paper
b) glass
c) thermosetting plastic
d) card   (1 mark)

5 Waste materials that are able to decompose easily in the environment are called:
a) biodegradable materials
b) non-biodegradable materials
c) packaging materials
d) toxic materials   (1 mark)

Score   / 5

B

Answer all parts of the questions.

Consider whether the following statements are true or false.

		True	False
1	A renewable resource is one that cannot be renewed within 500 years.	☐	☐
2	Softwood trees take longer to grow than hardwood trees.	☐	☐
3	Metals are a non-renewable resource.	☐	☐
4	Plastics are a renewable resource.	☐	☐
5	Manufacturing processes that use plastics tend to use less energy than manufacturing processes that use metals.	☐	☐
6	Paints that contain lead can be used to paint children's toys.	☐	☐
7	A thermoplastic cannot be recycled.	☐	☐

(7 marks)

Score   / 7

These are GCSE-style questions. Answer all parts of the questions.

1 The sketches show three common types of food packaging.

Package 1
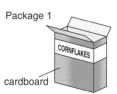
CORNFLAKES
cardboard

Package 2

shrink-wrap plastic
fruit

Package 3

Baked Beans
tin

a) Consider each of these types of packaging. Complete the table below.

Package	Type of Material Used	Is the Material Biodegradable?
1		
2		
3		

(6 marks)

b) Give three environmental factors that should be considered when designing packaging for products.

Factor 1 ....

Factor 2 ....

Factor 3 .... (3 marks)

2 You have been asked to give a five-minute talk on methods of reducing waste in your school workshop.

a) Give three points that you would make during your talk.

....

....

.... (3 marks)

b) Give two examples of a renewable energy source.

....

.... (2 marks)

c) Give two examples of a non-renewable energy resource.

....

.... (2 marks)

d) Explain why manufactured boards may be better for the environment as a whole than using natural timber.

....

....

.... (3 marks)

Score   / 19

How well did you do?

0–8 correct   Try again
9–17 correct   Getting there
18–23 correct   Good work
24–31 correct   Excellent!

TOTAL SCORE   / 31

For more information on this topic see pages 30–31 of your Success Guide

USE OF CAD

A

Choose just one answer, a, b, c or d.

1 CAD stands for:
   a) computer action design
   b) computer automated design
   c) computer aided design
   d) computer aided drawing   (1 mark)

2 Two-dimensional drawings are called:
   a) orthographic drawings b) solid models
   c) isometric drawings   d) pictorial drawings
                                        (1 mark)

3 Which of the following types of CAD packages
allow drawings to be rotated and viewed at
various angles?
   a) 2-D CAD packages
   b) standard parts packages
   c) solid modelling CAD packages
   d) working drawing CAD packages   (1 mark)

4 Which of the following types of drawings often
show how a product is assembled together?
   a) freehand sketching
   b) component drawing
   c) 2-D drawing
   d) exploded drawing   (1 mark)

5 Which of the following is not usually carried
out using CAD methods?
   a) 2-D drawings
   b) 3-D drawings
   c) initial design research sketches
   d) orthographic drawings   (1 mark)

Score   / 5

B

Answer all parts of the questions.

1 A computer plotter cutting machine is being used to
produce safety signs for a school workshop.

computer

WEAR GOGGLES

vinyl

cutting machine

a) Give four advantages of using the computer cutter rather than cutting the vinyl by hand.

....

....

....

....   (4 marks)

b) When might it be more beneficial to cut out the signs without the use of the computer system?

....

....   (2 marks)

c) Give two other ways in which a CAD package can be used directly to make products
in the school workshop.

....

....   (2 marks)

Score   / 8

These are GCSE-style questions. Answer all parts of the questions.

1 The diagram shows the main features of a box which is to be designed using a CAD system.

a) List three types of drawings that could be drawn using the CAD system and give one reason why each would be used in the design process.

....

....

.... (3 marks)

b) Explain how the CAD system could be used to make other similar boxes, with slight modifications, quickly and easily.

....

....

....

.... (4 marks)

c) Give two reasons why the CAD system can help reduce the time between the design process and manufacture.

....

.... (2 marks)

2 a) Explain how CAD packages can be used in addition to free-hand sketching in the design of products.

....

.... (2 marks)

b) How might the use of CAD speed up product manufacture?

....

....

....

.... (3 marks)

Score   / 14

How well did you do?

0–8 correct   Try again
9–14 correct   Getting there
15–22 correct   Good work
23–27 correct   Excellent!

TOTAL SCORE   / 27

For more information on this topic see pages 32–33 of your Success Guide

SYSTEMS AND CONTROL DESIGN

A Choose just one answer, a, b, c or d.

1 Which of the following gears is used to turn shafts at right angles to each other?
a) compound gears
b) rack and pinion gears
c) bevel gears
d) idler gears (1 mark)

2 Which type of gears can be used to change rotary motion into linear motion?
a) worm gears
b) rack and pinion gears
c) bevel gears
d) helical gears (1 mark)

3 Which type of belt drive results in no slippage during use?
a) toothed belts   b) smooth belts
c) vee belts   d) circular belts   (1 mark)

4 Reciprocating motion is often achieved using a:
a) helical gear mechanism
b) vee belt mechanism
c) cam mechanism
d) cog mechanism (1 mark)

5 Closed-loop systems normally include feedback:
a) sensors
b) gears
c) belt drives
d) bulbs (1 mark)

Score   / 5

B Answer all parts of the questions.

1 State whether these statements are true or false.

	True	False
a) An open-loop system is where there is some feedback to help control the system.	☐	☐
b) Closed-loop systems tend to be more accurate than open-loop systems.	☐	☐
c) Systems diagrams are block diagrams that show how the various parts of a system link together.	☐	☐
d) A quality check can be regarded as a feedback loop in a manufacturing system.	☐	☐

(4 marks)

2 The diagram shows a typical use of a cam mechanism. Complete the diagram by using these words to label the parts.

| slider | rotational motion | cam | cam follower | slider guide | reciprocating motion |

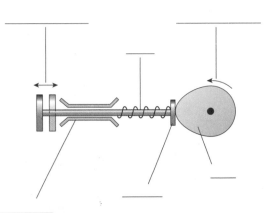

(6 marks)

Score   / 10

C These are GCSE-style questions. Answer all parts of the questions.

1 A small mechanism has been designed to help print some labels. To print, a label is pushed underneath the stamp and the lever is then pushed down.

a) Indicate on the diagram the position of the applied load, the effort and the pivot. (3 marks)

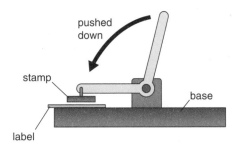

b) Show how the lever could be made to return automatically. (2 marks)

c) Design a simple method of moving the print plate at a constant rate to speed up the operation.

(6 marks)

2 a) Name three types of gears that are used in mechanisms.

....

....

.... (3 marks)

b) State two advantages of using gears rather than belt drives.

....

.... (2 marks)

c) Explain the difference between a simple gear train and a compound gear train.

....

....

.... (3 marks)

Score   / 19

How well did you do?

0–8 correct   Try again
9–15 correct   Getting there
16–22 correct   Good work
23–28 correct   Excellent!

TOTAL SCORE   / 28

For more information on this topic see pages 34–35 of your Success Guide

SAFE WORKING PROCEDURES

A Choose just one answer, a, b, c or d.

1 The kite mark is the symbol of:
a) British safety institute
b) British safety confederation
c) school safety group
d) British Standards Institute   (1 mark)

2 Assessing the potential dangers in a workshop prior to using hazardous substances, equipment and machinery is officially termed:
a) danger assessment
b) workshop assessment
c) machinery assessment
d) risk assessment   (1 mark)

3 The abbreviation COSHH stands for:
a) central office supporting health hazards
b) centre of social health hygiene
c) control of substances hazardous to health
d) controlling operational substances hazardous to health   (1 mark)

4 Which of the following should you not do when working on a drilling machine?
a) tie loose hair back   b) wear goggles
c) keep hands away from moving parts and cutters
d) leave chuck keys in the chuck   (1 mark)

5 Which of the following should you not do when working with hazardous materials?
a) wear protective gloves when handling hot metals
b) never spray paint in an unventilated room
c) dispose of chemical waste down the workshop sink
d) keep flammable chemicals and materials away from naked flames   (1 mark)

Score   / 5

B Answer all parts of the questions.

1 State four safety points that should be observed when working with others in the design and technology workshop.

Point 1 ....

Point 2 ....

Point 3 ....

Point 4 ....   (4 marks)

2 Choose one of these phrases to complete the following sentences.

| hands | eyes | tie | switching | guards | unattended |

a) Do not leave machines .... while they are in use.

b) Never adjust or clean a machine without .... it off and isolating it first.

c) Keep .... away from moving parts.

d) Always .... long hair back.

e) Always use the .... on the machines.

f) Always wear the correct protective clothing to protect .... , body and feet.

          (6 marks)

Score   / 10

38

These are GCSE-style questions. Answer all parts of the questions.

1 You are going to make a cassette rack like the one shown in the diagram. This will involve bending the rods around a former to shape, brazing the joints together and cleaning the joints with a file and emery cloth.

It will finally be sprayed up using paint.

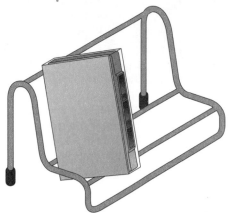

a) Complete the risk assessment sheet giving the potential risks for each stage of manufacture.

Operation	Description of Risks
Bending bars around jig	
Brazing the joints together	
Cleaning up joints with file	
Finishing off with emery cloth	
Paint-spraying the rack	

(6 marks)

b) Give two safety factors that should be considered to make the product safe for the home.

Safety Factor 1...

Safety Factor 2... (2 marks)

2 Give three safety factors that should be observed for these processes.

a) Chiselling a neat groove in wood.

....

.... (3 marks)

b) Turning down a piece of bar in a centre lathe.

....

.... (3 marks)

c) Moulding a lamp shade with fibre reinforced plastics.

....

.... (3 marks)

Score   / 17

How well did you do?

0–8 correct   Try again
9–17 correct   Getting there
18–25 correct   Good work
26–32 correct   Excellent!

TOTAL SCORE   **/ 32**

For more information on this topic see pages 38–39 of your Success Guide

PREPARATION FOR MANUFACTURE

A Choose just one answer, a, b, c or d.

1 All accurate marking out should start from:
a) an edge line   b) a datum line
c) a date line   d) a square line   (1 mark)

2 Which of the following is not a tool used for the marking out of metals or plastics?
a) scriber
b) odd-leg callipers
c) marking gauge
d) scribing block   (1 mark)

3 Round bars can be firmly held for marking out with the aid of a:
a) G-clamp
b) bench block
c) vee-block and clamp
d) section clamp   (1 mark)

4 Try squares are used to mark lines out at:
a) 90 degrees to a datum surface
b) parallel to a datum surface
c) 45 degrees to a datum surface
d) 60 degrees to a datum surface   (1 mark)

5 Which tool should be used when marking lines across the grain of wood?
a) marking knife
b) scriber
c) centre punch
d) chisel   (1 mark)

Score   / 5

B Answer all parts of the questions.

1 Complete the table below. State which tool should be used for each process.

Material	Activity	Tool Used
Wood	marking lines parallel to the datum	
Metal and plastics	marking arcs and circles	
Wood	producing the face side datum	
Metal and plastics	producing a datum face using a hand tool	
Metal and plastics	finding the centre of a round bar	
Metals	marking lines on the metal	
Plastics	marking lines on brittle plastics	

(7 marks)

2 State three reasons why marking out is generally carried out when working in the workshop.

Reason 1   ....

Reason 2   ....

Reason 3   ....   (3 marks)

Score   / 10

These are GCSE-style questions. Answer all parts of the questions.

1 A small name plate is to be made in your design and technology workshop. It can be made from either a metal, plastics or wood material.

D & T
DEPARTMENT

With the aid of neat sketches show how each material would be marked out.
Your answer should state the particular tools used for each of the materials.

Metal	Plastics	Wood

(9 marks)

2 Briefly explain how you would mark out the following.

a) A parallel line to one of the faces of a piece of timber wood that has not been planed.

....

.... (2 marks)

b) A line on a piece of BDMS that is to be machined.

....

.... (2 marks)

c) A circle on a piece of acrylic plastics.

....

.... (2 marks)

Score   / 15

PREPARATION FOR MANUFACTURE

How well did you do?

0–7 correct   Try again
8–16 correct   Getting there
17–22 correct Good work
23–30 correct Excellent!

TOTAL SCORE   / 30

For more information on this topic
see pages 40–41 of your Success Guide

HAND TOOLS FOR METALS AND PLASTICS

A Choose just one answer a, b, c, d.

1 A smooth finish on metals is often achieved using:
a) draw filing
b) push filing
c) pull finishing
d) pull filing   (1 mark)

2 Curved shapes can be cut using:
a) cutting saw
b) curving saw
c) coping saw
d) chain saw   (1 mark)

3 The name given to the small version of the hacksaw is:
a) juvenile hacksaw
b) miniature hacksaw
c) junior hacksaw
d) model hacksaw   (1 mark)

4 Small files used for precise and accurate work such as filing jewellery are:
a) rough cut files
b) dreadnought files
c) needle files
d) coping files   (1 mark)

5 When using a hacksaw the cutting action occurs on:
a) the backward stroke
b) the backward and forward strokes
c) the vertical stroke
d) the forward stroke   (1 mark)

Score   / 5

B Answer all parts of the questions.

1 The table shows some of the common types of file cross-sections. Complete the table.   (4 marks)

Cross-section	Name of File	Use
 ▬		
■		
 ▲		
 ●		

2 You have been asked to buy some tools for some design and technology tasks.
For each task give a specification for the tool. An example has been given to help you.

A hacksaw for cutting thin steel tubes.   A hacksaw with 12 teeth/cm.

a) A file for the initial filing of soft metals and plastics.

....

b) A hacksaw for general cutting of plastics.

....

c) A chisel for cleaning out corners of square holes in metal products.

....

d) A file for getting a good final finish on hard materials.

....   (4 marks)

Score   / 8

These are GCSE-style questions. Answer all parts of the questions.

1 As part of a robot project in your school workshop you have been asked to make a small hinge out of mild steel sectional bar. The tools that you can use are hacksaw, range of files and a cold chisel.

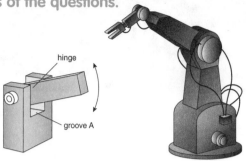

hinge

groove A

a) Use neat diagrams to explain how you would cut out groove A in the diagram.

(3 marks)

b) Give two safety precautions that should be taken into account when using the tools.

....

.... (2 marks)

c) Use diagrams to show how a smooth finish can be achieved once the groove has been cut.

(3 marks)

2 You have been asked to cut out a small free-form jewellery shape from a piece of plastics material. The shape has already been marked out ready for cutting. Explain how you would cut out and finish the shape using hand tools.

....

....

....

....

....

.... (6 marks)

Score   / 14

How well did you do?

0–7 correct   Try again
8–13 correct   Getting there
14–21 correct   Good work
22–27 correct   Excellent!

TOTAL SCORE   / 27

For more information on this topic
see pages 42–43 of your Success Guide

HAND TOOLS FOR WOOD

A

Choose just one answer, a, b, c or d.

1 Which of the following is not a type of plane?
a) jack plane
b) smoothing plane
c) mortice plane
d) rebate plane (1 mark)

2 Which of these is a tool that is used specifically to plane curved surfaces?
a) axle shave   b) spoke shave
c) circle shave   d) wheel shave (1 mark)

3 A chisel used to cut wood out from the corners of a joint is called a:
a) cold chisel
b) corner chisel
c) shoulder chisel
d) bevel-edged chisel (1 mark)

4 Large holes, such as 30 mm diameter, can be drilled using a:
a) hole saw
b) ripsaw
c) diameter saw
d) brace saw (1 mark)

5 A common type of saw for general work in the design and technology workshop is a:
a) wood saw
b) craft saw
c) tenon saw
d) plough saw (1 mark)

Score   / 5

B

Answer all parts of the questions.

1 With the aid of a neat sketch explain how you could plane across the grain of a piece of wood without splitting the wood.

(4 marks)

2 The first column of the table below describes four types of specialist planes.

Complete the table stating the purpose of each of the planes. The first has been done for you.

Type of Plane	Use of Plane
Shoulder plane	*for finishing off shoulders and square corners*
Plough plane	
Rebate plane	
Spokeshave	

(6 marks)

Score   / 10

These are GCSE-style questions. Answer all parts of the questions.

1 a) The side shape of a one-off wooden toy has been marked out ready for making.

Complete the flow chart below describing the stages that you would use in its manufacture. Include in your descriptions the name of the tools that you would use.

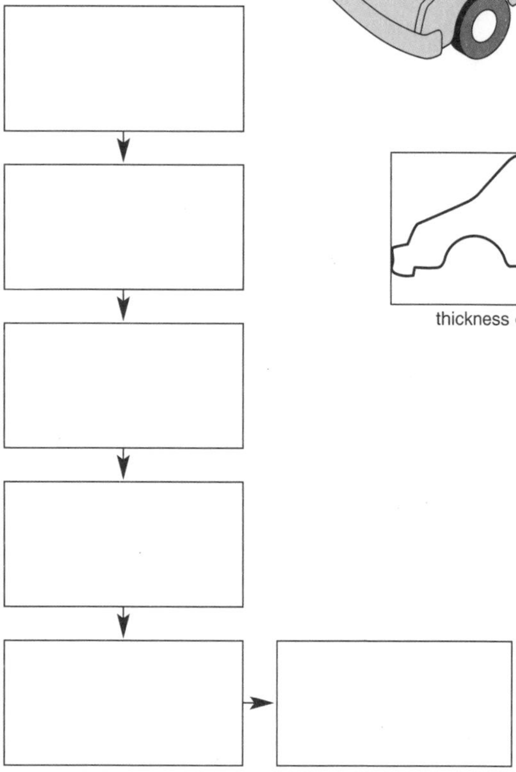

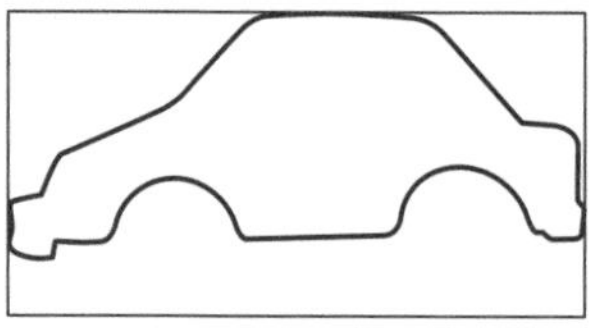

thickness of side = 6 mm

(6 marks)

b) Select two of the stages you have described. Give the safety precautions that need to be observed during that stage of manufacture.

....

....

....

.... (2 marks)

2 a) Name two types of saws used to cut timber and give one use for each.

....

.... (2 marks)

b) Give three ways in which a range of hole sizes could be made in wood.

....

....

.... (3 marks)

Score   / 13

How well did you do?

0–8 correct   Try again
9–14 correct   Getting there
15–22 correct   Good work
23–28 correct   Excellent!

TOTAL SCORE   / 28

For more information on this topic see pages 44–45 of your Success Guide

MACHINE TOOLS FOR METALS AND PLASTICS

A

Choose just one answer a), b), c) or d).

1 Which of the following is not a machine tool operation for metal and plastics?
   a) milling machine
   b) centre lathe
   c) routing machine
   d) pillar drilling machine   (1 mark)

2 Many lathe tools are made from:
   a) high speed steel
   b) mild steel   c) cast iron
   d) high density polypropylene   (1 mark)

3 Turning down a round bar on a centre lathe is a type of:
   a) reforming process
   b) re-grinding process
   c) re-generating process
   d) wasting process   (1 mark)

4 Which of the following tools is not used in a pillar drill?
   a) countersink bit
   b) counterboring tool
   c) hole saw
   d) facing off tool   (1 mark)

5 A white liquid used to reduce the heat and friction when machining some metals is commonly called:
   a) heatsink
   b) coolwhite
   c) coolant
   d) reducant   (1 mark)

Score   / 5

B

Answer all parts of the question.

1 a) The diagrams below show four common operations that are carried out on a centre lathe. Name the operation that is being carried out in each case.

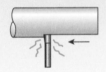 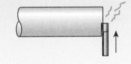  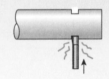

....   (4 marks)

b) The diagram shows a round bar.

   On the diagram, sketch the correct position of a lathe tool to ensure that it machines properly.

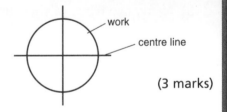

   (3 marks)

c) Indicate which kind of chuck is used with each kind of bar.

Type of Bar	Three-Jaw or Four-Jaw Chuck
Round bar	
Octagonal bar	
Hexagonal bar	
Square bar	

(4 marks)

Score   / 11

C These are GCSE-style questions. Answer all parts of the questions.

1 The plastic spindle shown in the diagram below is to be machined on a lathe and then drilled using a pillar drill to produce the hole.

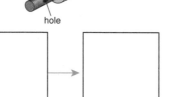

a) Using the flow diagram below, complete the stages of the process. The first stage has been completed for you.

Clamp in lathe chuck	→		→		→		→	

(5 marks)

b) Give three safety precautions that must be observed when carrying out the machining operations.

....

....

.... (3 marks)

c) Give three reasons why it is better to use the machine tools rather than using hand tools and a hand drill to perform the operations.

....

....

.... (3 marks)

d) What is the best drill point angle for the operation?

.... (1 mark)

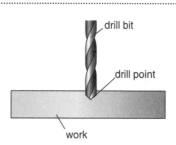

2 Which machine tools would you use for the following operations?

a) Machining a flat surface.. (1 mark)

b) Facing off a piece of round bar... (1 mark)

c) Countersinking a hole in a piece of wood... (1 mark)

d) Explain the use of coolants when machining certain materials.

....

....

.... (3 marks)

Score / 18

How well did you do?

0–10 correct   Try again
11–19 correct   Getting there
20–27 correct   Good work
28–34 correct   Excellent!

TOTAL SCORE   / 34

For more information on this topic
see pages 46–47 of your Success Guide

MACHINE TOOLS FOR WOOD

A

Choose just one answer, a, b, c or d.

1 Which of the following is not a wood machine tool?
a) circular saw
b) band saw
c) sanding machine
d) milling machine   (1 mark)

2 Curved shapes are often sawn using a:
a) tape saw
b) band saw
c) wood turning lathe
d) curving saw   (1 mark)

3 Large sheets of wood are often cut using a:
a) sheet saw
b) toothed saw
c) circular saw
d) radius saw   (1 mark)

4 An electrical hand tool that uses a short reciprocating blade to cut the wood is called an:
a) electrical jig saw
b) electrical blade saw
c) electrical slotting saw
d) electrical hand saw   (1 mark)

5 The wood on a wood turning lathe is very often clamped to a:
a) face plate
b) front plate
c) forward plate
d) fixing plate   (1 mark)

Score   / 5

B

Answer all parts of the questions.

Choose one of these phrases to complete the sentences below.

| circular saw | dust | trained teachers | extreme caution | goggles |

1 You will be very unlikely to use a .... or band saw in the school workshop.

2 Circular saws and band saws are mainly used by .... and technicians.

3 When using wood machines .... should be worn at all times.

4 The .... from wood machining operations is a health hazard especially when using manufactured boards.

5 .... must be taken when using wood machine tools to reduce the risk of serious accidents and dust inhalation.

(5 marks)

Score   / 5

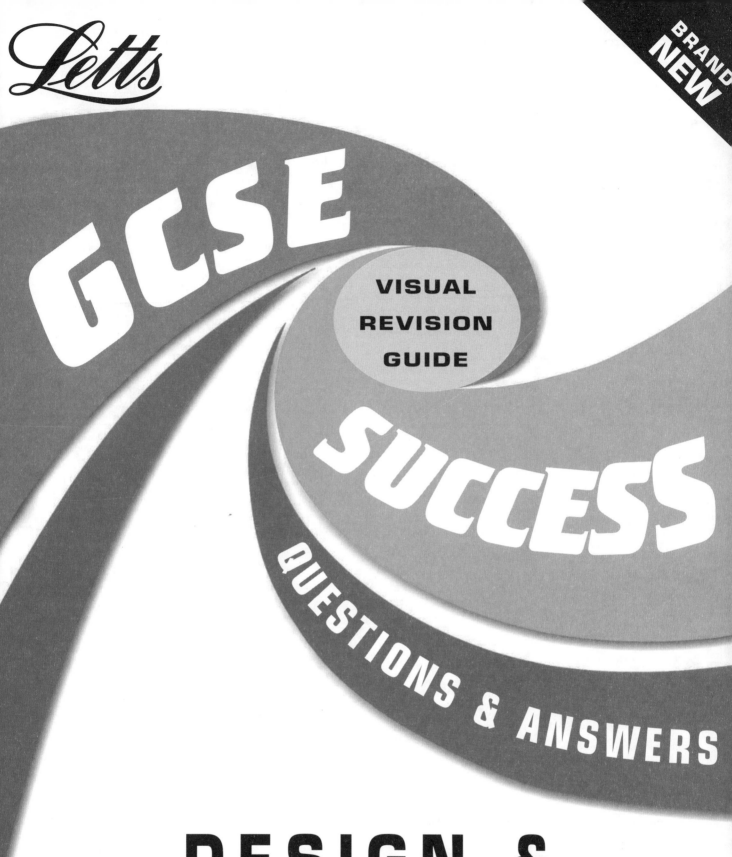

Letts

GCSE SUCCESS

VISUAL
REVISION
GUIDE

QUESTIONS & ANSWERS

BRAND NEW

DESIGN &
TECHNOLOGY

Chris Hughes

ANSWER BOOK

MATERIALS AND COMPONENTS

PROPERTIES OF MATERIALS

A
1 c 2 b 3 a
4 a 5 c

B
1 a) true b) true
  c) false d) true
  e) false
2 a) machineability
  b) cold-worked
  c) ductile
  d) malleability

C
1 a) A property is a characteristic of a material.
  b) i) plastic/urea formaldehyde
     ii) brass
     iii) copper
     iv) plastics, type PVC
  c)

Part	Two Properties
Body	good electrical insulator, tough, good strength properties, able to be moulded
Conducting pins	ductile for extrusion, good conductor of electricity, tough, hard-wearing
Conducting wires	ductile to be made into wire, good conductor of electricity, non-corrosive
Insulation on the wires	good insulator of electricity, reasonable strength properties, flexible

2 a)

Product	Two Properties
Pole-vaulting pole	good bending strength, good resistance against degradation, good compressive and tensile strength, good elasticity properties
Rock-climbing rope	good tensile strength, good degradation properties
Hockey stick	needs to be flexible, good strength properties, good degradation properties, relatively hard, springy
Running shoes	good degradation properties, good strength properties, hard-wearing
Tennis racket frame	good strength properties, hard-wearing, small amount of flexibility

  b) Each piece of equipment needs to withstand impact-type loads. If the materials were not tough they would suddenly break on impact.

MATERIAL CHOICE IN DESIGN

A
1 c 2 a 3 c
4 d 5 a

B
1 a) Good resistance to corrosion, good toughness, good wear resistance, good strength properties.
  b) Can be moulded, good flow properties.
  c) The whole frame can be moulded in one piece. Plastics tend to require less energy to make the product than by making in metal. It can be made in one piece and fewer processes are required. Plastic items may not need as much finishing as metal product. Plastic does not need spraying.

C
1 a) Answers could include: cost of buying the wooden parts, cost of cutting the parts to length, cost of machining, cost of finishing and painting, cost of quality checks, cost of packaging and transport.
  b) Answers could include: whether the paint is toxic or not, whether the wood would splinter, and when to use softwoods in preference to hardwoods since they take a shorter time to regrow.
  c) The standard sections can be bought easily from suppliers. The sections can be simply measured for length and then cut. There is no need to machine the parts to size.

2 a) Must be rigid and not flex too much, must be strong enough to carry the weight of the child, must be hard wearing and durable so that it will not break in use.
  b) What skills are required to make the various parts, what machines and tools are available in the workshop, what materials are to be used.
  c) The manufacturing and material costs, the materials that are available, the types of finish that is required.

MATERIAL FORMS

A
1 c 2 a 3 b
4 d 5 d

B
1 standard stock sizes
2 manufacturers' catalogues
3 volume
4 cross-sections
5 accurate finish
6 lathe chuck

C
1 a) round section
  b) Answers could include: can be bought easily from catalogues, can be held in lathes and vices without further work, does not need any machining to get ready for use, cheaper than machining down from bar.
  c) Answer to include clear diagram. Turn down the bar on lathe. Undercut the bar for thread. Part-off the bar. Use stock and die to put thread. Check thread to make sure that nut will fit on it. If not run die down again.
  d) Put the round section bar into lathe. Face off the end to make bar flat. Centre drill and drill bar to make the hole. Part-off on lathe and clean up burrs with a file.

2 a)

Application	Material Form
Vacuum-formed boxes	sheet plastic material
Plastic labels to stick onto the boxes	label for sticker materials
Material to make reinforced plastic products	plastic resin
Material for injection moulding machine	powder or granules
Metal for decorative forge work	black mild steel
12 mm bar for general lathe work	bright drawn mild steel
Wood for making toy car axles	wooden dowelling

  b) The bar has an accurate finish and can be fitted straight into machine vices and chucks for manufacturing. The accurate finish makes good datum surfaces.

METALS 1

A
1 c 2 b 3 d
4 b 5 d

B
1 a) Alloys are mixtures of two or more pure metals.
  b) Pure metals contain only one type of metal.
  c) Alloys tend to be stronger than pure metals.
  d) Alloys tend to have better physical properties than pure metals.
2 Hardness and toughness will increase. Ductility will decrease.

C
1 a)

Use	Metal
Food cans	tin plate
Metal work vices	cast iron
Drill bits for wood	high carbon steel
Kitchen sinks	stainless steel
The pins of a 13-amp plug	brass
The wire in electrical cables	copper

  b) Answers could include: good conductor of heat, does not corrode, lightweight, can be formed relatively easily.
  c) Answers could include: paint, plastics coating, galvanising.
2 a) Ductile so it can be bent easily, malleable so that it can be formed into shape, easily joined, corrosion resistant.
  b) brass
  c) solder
  d) tin and lead

METALS 2

A
1 c 2 a 3 a
4 d 5 a

B
1

Metal	Carbon Content
Cast iron	3.5%-4.5% carbon
High carbon steel	0.8%-1.5% carbon
Mild steel	0.15%-0.35% carbon
Medium carbon steel	0.3%-0.7% carbon

2

Material	Composition
Mild steel	iron and carbon
Bronze	copper and tin
Duralumin	aluminium and copper
Solder	tin and lead
Stainless steel	iron, carbon and chromium and/or nickel

C
1 a) stainless steel, aluminium
  b) ABS
  c) Answers include: good strength properties, tough, good resistance to corrosion, can withstand relatively high temperatures, hygienic and can be cleaned.
  d) Answers include: good strength properties, tough, good resistance to corrosion, can withstand relatively high temperatures, hygienic and can be cleaned.
  e) Answers include: needs to be pressed into shape which is a high-energy process, is not an electrical insulating material, cannot be coloured, parts have to be welded together.

HEAT TREATMENT PROCESSES

A
1 b 2 a 3 c
4 a 5 c

B
1 a) true b) true
  c) true d) false
2 When a metal is hammered it will tend to become harder. As the metal becomes harder it becomes more difficult to work. It will eventually become so hard that further hammering cannot be done. Annealing softens the metal so that further hammering can take place.

C
1 a) When a metal is being bent it will work harden. Annealing will soften the metal so that it does not crack or break when bending.
  b) Rub soap on the aluminium. The soap will turn black at the correct annealing temperature.
  c) Aluminium will melt.
  d) Wear leather safety apron, wear correct eye protection, make sure flame is directed to brazing hearth and not to others in workshop, use tongs to pick up hot metal.
2 a) high carbon steel
  b) The point is firstly heated up using a brazing torch up to cherry red. Once this temperature has been reached it is quenched in water or oil. This hardens the metal. The next stage is tempering. For this the point is re-heated to the correct tempering temperature and then quenched in water.
  c) Tempering removes the brittleness so that the tool can be used without the point snapping.

PLASTICS

A
1 d 2 d 3 c
4 d 5 d

B 1

Process	Type of plastic
Plastic extrusion	thermoplastic
Transfer moulding	thermosetting
Vacuum forming	thermoplastic
Compression moulding	thermosetting
Blow moulding	thermoplastic
Injection moulding	thermoplastic

2

Plastic	Type	Two Uses
Polystyrene	thermoplastic	packaging, disposable cups, plates, picnic boxes, model toys
Urea formaldehyde	thermosetting	electrical fittings, electrical switches
Melamine formaldehyde	thermosetting	work surfaces, kitchenware
Polythene	thermoplastic	detergent bottles, carrier bags, food packaging, outside cover of cables
Polyvinyl chloride (PVC)	thermoplastic	pipes and gutters, window frames
Nylon	thermoplastic	knock-down fittings, bearings, gears, ropes

C
a) Thermoplastic
b) Polythene or polystyrene
c) Answers could include: can be moulded easily, can be coloured, will not corrode, can be cleaned easily, is reasonably tough, good chemical resistance, can be used for foodstuffs.
2 a) Hard material, rigid and stiff, good electrical insulator, good strength properties, good heat-resistant properties.
b) Compression moulding or transfer moulding.
c) Curing forms cross-links between the main polymer chains. This makes the plastic more rigid and increases its toughness and strength.

WOODS

A
1 d 2 c 3 d
4 b 5 b

B
1

Timber	Softwood or Hardwood	Use
Ash	hardwood	tool handles, hockey sticks, ladders
Beech	hardwood	chairs, work benches, tool handles
Oak	hardwood	garden furniture, boat hulls, high-quality indoor furniture
Spruce	softwood	internal door frames, furniture

2 Softwoods come from coniferous trees which mature more quickly than hardwood trees. The softwood trees can be replaced at a much quicker rate than hardwood trees which is better for the environment.
3 Examples include: plywood, chipboard, veneer, medium density fibreboard (MDF), blockboard, hardboard.

C
1 a) Advantages include: available in large sheets, not affected by humidity, can be used with different-coloured veneers, do not have problems with grain when working, more easily worked than many natural timbers, can be easily joined with knock-down fittings.
b) Reasons include: better appearance, does not require veneering, higher-quality product required.
c) Answers include: dry rot, wet rot, insect attack.
d) Answers include: varnish, stain, paint.
2 a) Hardwoods – oak, beech, ash. Softwoods – western red cedar.
b) Splits – slits in the timber, shrinkage due to it not being seasoned properly, knots – which may cause problems when joining or machining.
c) Caused by wet and damp conditions where the wood becomes weak and spongy. This can be prevented by painting or using an outside wood preservative.

COMPOSITE MATERIALS AND SMART MATERIALS

A
1 c 2 a
3 d 4 a
5 d

B
1 Answers include: sports equipment, chemical vessels and pipework, transport applications, boat hulls, bullet-proof vests, crash helmets, aircraft parts.

---

2 a) true b) false
c) true d) false
e) true

C

length 3 metres
thickness 20 mm

1 a) First, release agent is applied to the mould. Then a layer of plastics resin is applied by a brush or roller to build up the first layer of the boat hull. A layer of fibre matting is moulded into the resin. Further layers of resin and fibre are built up until the required thickness has been reached. The hull is left to set. Then it is released from the mould and cleaned up using hand tools.
b) Answers include: quicker, will not need a coat with a wood preservative, needs little maintenance.
c) Glass fibre and plastic.

2 a) Do not corrode, are lighter, can be made easier and cheaper.
b) Glass reinforced plastics.
c) Filament winding.
d) More constant quality, quicker method, more accurate pipe produced.

COMPONENTS AND ADHESIVES

A
1 d 2 c 3 d
4 b 5 a

B
1

Type of Adhesive	Use
Polyvinyl acetate (PVA)	general wood joints
Cascamite	where waterproofing is required
Araldite	can bond metals or plastic parts
Tensol (acrylic cement)	used to cement together certain plastic parts

2
wing nut

castle nut

fibre insert locknut

locknut

3 Answers include: ensure that gluing surfaces are clean, the surface is free from dirt, the surface is free from moisture, use the correct adhesive for the job, use clamps to apply pressure to the joint, clean excess glue from the joint before the glue sets.

C
1 a) Temporary
b) Use temporary fixing so that the wheel can be

---

removed for maintenance, can change the wheels when they wear out.

c)
fibre insert
locknut

Use locknut which has nylon insert to prevent it working loose due to vibrations.
2 a) Self-tapping screws are made from a hardened steel and are able to cut their own thread when screwed into pre-drilled metal.
b) To protect the product surfaces from damage when nuts and bolts are tightened.
c) The thread on a bolt does not go all the way to the head. There is a plain diameter at the head end. The thread of a set screw goes all the way to the head of the screw.

DESIGN AND MARKET INFLUENCES

PRODUCT ANALYSIS

A
1 a 2 c 3 d
4 c 5 c

B
1

Materials
What materials are used?
Reasons for their choice.
Details of finishing.

Assembly
Description of the fixings that are used.
How parts locate in place.
How can the product be taken apart for maintenance and changing parts?

Manufacturing
What are the main production routes?
Reasons for choosing the routes.
Details of quantities manufactured/sold.

Environmental issues
Can parts of the product be recycled?
Are any parts made from biodegradable materials?
Is the product safe to use?
Are any environmentally unfriendly processes used in its production?

What to include in an analysis

Working principles
Does the project incorporate any mechanisms?
If so, how does it work?
How are the mechanisms maintained?
How reliable is the product?

Aesthetics and ergonomics

Background to the product
The name and type of product.
A description of its intended use.
How the product works and how it is used.
Photographs, sketches, diagrams of product.
Short description of the parts and how it is assembled.
Exploded views of the parts.

C
1 a) Answers to include:

Materials	Environmental Factors	Assembly
Type used, mechanical properties such as toughness, wear ability and strength, colour, and finish	Whether it requires regular maintenance, corrosion properties, whether it is environmentally friendly	How the parts are assembled, what parts are used, for example bearings and bushes, whether the wheels are attached permanently or by temporary fittings

b) Examples include hair dryers, mobile phones, transistor radios, electric kettles, smoke alarms. Reasons for choice include: may be disassembled to look at parts, range of materials and processes used in their construction, small number of parts used.
2 a) To gain an understanding of how the product works, what materials have been used, how parts fit together and what manufacturing processes have been used.
b) Description of the product, its purpose, working principles, safety features, ergonomic and aesthetic features, manufacturing routes and costs, any environmental factors.

GENERATING DESIGN PROPOSALS

A
1 b 2 d 3 b
4 c 5 b

B
1 Choose an area of study (context) from which a project need can be found
Define the project need
Prepare a design brief
Write a specification for the project
Carry out research to help in the initial design stages
Select the best idea or ideas for further development. Give reasons for choices.
2 Reason 1 To keep up with fashion changes, for example mobile phones.
Reason 2 To improve existing products.
Reason 3 To improve a product's safety features.
Reason 4 To keep up with new technologies.

C
1 a) Answers to include: how the product will be used, its colour, size and shape, ergonomic factors, reliability factors, maintenance requirements.
b) Answers to include: the quantity of the products to be made, what machines and tools are available, what people are available, the quality specifications of the product, the timescale for manufacture, the cost limitations of the product.
c) Modelling helps to look at factors such as proportion, how the parts may fit together and how the parts may be machined and manufactured.
2 a) Addition of new safety features, fashion may have changed, the company may use a policy of planned obsolescence, improvement of existing phones, to keep up with other companies, to keep up with changes in technology.
b) The size of the phone, colour, what it is intended to do, how the battery will be changed and how it will be programmed, aesthetic factors, ergonomic factors, etc.

c) Market research to find out factors such as what colours are popular, size of hands for different age and gender groups. Investigating other phones on the market.

PRODUCT DEVELOPMENT AND PLANNING

A

1 d   2 a   3 c
4 a   5 b

B

1 Planning is essential to plan the manufacturing route, the manufacturing times and how the quality of the product will be controlled. Computer aided design is widely used to produce the final working drawing. Development makes use of sketches, further research and mock-ups to refine ideas. During the product development stage, work is carried out to transform the final design proposal into working drawings.

2 Answers could include: accurate measurements can be worked out, helps with ergonomic and aesthetic decision making, quicker and cheaper to produce than to produce the final product, can visualise in 3D form.

3 Answers could include: consider the aesthetic and ergonomic details, finalise cost and price, finalise materials, consider health and safety issues, consider environmental issues, consider assembly and manufacturing factors, show how final product will function.

C

1 a) cut the wood to the correct dimensions, locate in CNC machine, machine grooved housings, cut racks, assemble racks, check quality of racks.

b)

```
cut wood → locate in CNC machine → machine grooved housings / cut racks → assemble racks → check quality of racks
```

c) The batch quantity, the materials used, the finish required, tools available.

2 a) Design Aesthetics is concerned with the appearance of products. This will include aspects of colour, texture, style, form and shape.

b) Ergonomics relates the product being designed to suit the user.

c) Planning is required to ensure that the product can be designed, made and despatched successfully and also on time. Planning is essential for a number of reasons. These include making sure that materials and equipment are available for manufacture, that the design will work when made, that the product will be made at the right cost and that the manufacturing process is in the right sequence.

SOCIAL AND ENVIRONMENTAL CARE

A

1 c   2 c   3 b
     4 c   5 a

B

1 false
2 false
3 true
4 false
5 true
6 false
7 false

C

1 a)

Package	Type of Material Used	Is the Material Biodegradable?
1	cardboard	biodegradable
2	plastics	non-biodegradable
3	tin coated mild steel	non-biodegradable

b) Answers could include: whether the product has been recycled, whether it will harm the environment, whether the material is harmful to people, for example lead paints, the scarcity of the resource.

2 a) Make sure that sheet metals are marked out with minimal waste, use templates to mark out material in an efficient way, use stock bars to the nearest size for your jobs, use standard components where possible, where possible use plastics products since they generally require less energy to process.

b) Wind power, water power, solar energy and power.

c) Coal, oil, gas.

d) Manufactured boards are made from recycled and reconstituted wood. This means that fewer trees are cut down and used.

USE OF CAD

A

1 c   2 a   3 c
4 d   5 c

B

1 a) Answers could be: more accurate, higher quality achieved, quicker, constant product quality.

b) When a small batch is required, when one cannot afford the cost of buying the machine.

c) Plotter cutters, engraving machines.

C

1 a) Orthographic drawings show necessary dimensions, pictorial drawings give realistic idea of what final product would look like, exploded drawings show how parts fit together.

b) Can have standard parts in memory, make changes on drawing quickly, rearrange standard parts easily and quickly to redesign the box.

c) Information can be downloaded directly to the machine, different programs can be stored easily and changed quickly for different products and batch sizes.

2 a) Free-hand sketching is good for getting down initial ideas and exploring early design alternatives.

Once the design has been refined CAD can be used to help make computer solid models, make the orthographic and detail drawings. This tends to be much quicker and produces accurate drawings. Parts and drawings can be easily stored on disk.

b) CAD design computers can be directly linked to the manufacturing machines. Once a CAD design has been made the details can be automatically downloaded to the machine for manufacture.

SYSTEMS AND CONTROL DESIGN

A

1 c   2 b   3 a
4 c   5 a

B

1 a) false
   b) true
   c) true
   d) true

2

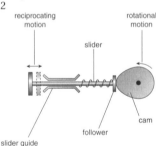

C

1 a)/b)

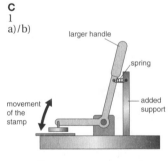

c) Show your answer to your teacher.

2 a) Answers could include: spur, rack and pinion, bevel, worm gears.

b) Can generally drive shafts with more power, can drive shafts which are very close together, they do not slip, belt drives tend to loosen after time.

c) Simple gear train just has two gears or three gears if an idler gear is required. Compound gear trains have more than two/three gears in the system.

MANUFACTURING PROCESSES

SAFE WORKING PROCEDURES

A

1 d   2 d   3 c
4 d   5 c

B

1 Move around safely, never run or fool around, carry tools safely, never work machines without permission, take care to protect others from dangers, keep workshop tidy, know the positions of the emergency stops.

2 a) Do not leave machines unattended while they are in use.

b) Never adjust or clean a machine without switching it off and isolating it first.

c) Keep hands away from moving parts.

d) Always tie long hair back.

e) Always use the guards on the machines.

f) Always wear the correct protective clothing to protect eyes, body and feet.

C

1 a)

Operation	Description of Risks
Bending bars around jig	strain on hands, might slip on the jig, jig may drop (low risk)
Brazing the joints together	risk from burns, possible danger from flames, risk from heat flash (high risk)
Cleaning up joints with file	danger from poorly maintained tools, possible sharp burrs (high risk)
Finishing off with emery cloth	risk from burrs (low risk)
Paint-spraying the rack	ventilation problems, paint in eyes, toxic problems

b) Never use toxic-type paints, file and remove all burrs, no sharp edges.

2 a) Keep both hands behind the front of the chisel when working, use a sharp chisel so that it cuts properly, make sure that there is space between you and others when you are cutting.

b) Wear goggles, make sure that the guard is down, make sure that work is correctly positioned in lathe, make sure that tool bit and work are tight in their positions, make sure that others are clear of the rotating parts of the lathe.

c) Wear a dust mask to prevent breathing in fibres, wear protective gloves, make sure that work space is well ventilated.

PREPARATION FOR MANUFACTURE

A

1 b   2 c   3 c
4 a   5 a

B 1

Material	Activity	Tool Used
Wood	marking lines parallel to the datum	marking gauge
Metal and plastics	marking arcs and circles	pair of dividers
Wood	producing the face side datum	plane
Metal and plastics	producing a datum face using a hand tool	file
Metal and plastics	finding the centre of a round bar	centre square
Metals	marking lines on the metal	scriber
Plastics	marking lines on brittle plastics	felt-tipped pen

2 Answers include: define the shape of an object, indicate the position of holes, keep waste to a minimum.

C 1

Metal	Plastics	Wood
A datum face would be marked. The metal would firstly be painted with engineer's marking blue. A centre datum line would be marked using rule and scriber. The end lines would be put on using an engineer's square. Parallel lines would be added using odd-leg callipers. Point would be put on using scriber. 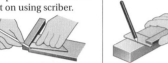	Similar tools would be used to metal. A wax crayon or felt-tipped pen would be used to mark out lines.	A datum face would be marked out and planed up. Cross-grain lines would be marked with a pencil and marking knife. Other lines would be marked out with a marking gauge.

2 a) Plane up the edge of the timber. Use a marking gauge set at the correct measurement to mark the line parallel to the face.
b) Brush or smear marking blue over the area to be marked out. Let the blue dry. Use a rule and engineer's try square to mark out line. Lightly centre punch on the line so that it can be seen when machining.
c) Put masking tape over centre of circle to be marked out. Use a pair of compasses with a felt-tip pen inserted. Mark off the centre of the circle with the felt-tip pen – going over the masking tape. Draw circle with pair of compasses. Keep point on the masking tape but do not press on hard otherwise the point can weaken the brittle acrylic material.

HAND TOOLS FOR METALS AND PLASTICS

A
1 a   2 c   3 c
4 c   5 d

B
1

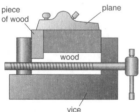

	Flat	used for general work
	Square	used for finishing square and rectangular holes and slots
	Three square	a triangular file for filing out sharp corners and internal angles
	Round	used for filing out holes

2 a) double-cut, rough file
b) hacksaw 5–6 teeth/cm
c) diamond point chisel
d) smooth file, double-cut

C
1 a) Hacksaw would be used to cut down the side slots. A cross-cut file would be used to clean out excess metal. Second cut file used to file shape to size.
b) Ensure that handles are on the tools, keep hands behind chisels when working, check hacksaw blades are not chipped, wear goggles when chiselling.
c) Achieve smooth finish by draw filing down, using emery cloth wrapped around the file.

2 Place plastics carefully in a vice. Use wood or soft vice jaws to prevent damaging the sides of the plastics. Carefully cut around the plastics using a coping saw or other suitable method. Use a second cut file to smooth down plastics to line. The cross-section of the line will depend upon the shape being made. Draw file edges to finish. Use emery cloth to remove all the final marks.

HAND TOOLS FOR WOOD

A
1 c   2 b   3 d
4 a   5 c

B
1 To avoid splitting the wood, pieces of wood can be clamped across the edges of the wood. This will ensure that the grain is squeezed together when being planed.

2

Type of Plane	Use of Plane
Shoulder plane	for finishing off shoulders and square corners
Plough plane	cutting grooves
Rebate plane	producing rebate shoulders
Spokeshave	for planing curved surfaces

C
1 a) Ask your teacher to check your answer.
b) Answers could include these typical safety precautions: safety with chisels, keeping hands behind chisel when working; using correct tools, appropriate safety clothing.
2 a) Ripsaws used for cutting in the direction of the grain.

Cross cut saws used for cutting across the grain and also for cutting manufactured boards. Tenon saws used for cutting small pieces of wood. Dovetail saws used for cutting dovetails. Coping saws used for cutting curves.
b) Small holes can be drilled using twist drill bits in pillar drill or hand drill. Larger holes can be drilled with a brace and bit. Large holes can be drilled with a hole saw where sizes can be changed accordingly.

MACHINE TOOLS FOR METALS AND PLASTICS

A
1 c   2 a   3 d
4 d   5 c

B
1 a) turning down, facing off, drilling, parting off
b)

c)

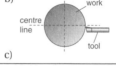

Type of Bar	Three-Jaw or Four-Jaw Chuck
Round bar	three-jaw
Octagonal bar	four-jaw
Hexagonal bar	three-jaw
Square bar	four-jaw

C
1 a)

clamp in lathe chuck	→	turn down ends of bar to size	→	mark hole using pencil and masking tape	→	clamp in drill machine vice	→	drill hole

b) Include clamping the bar down safely using vee blocks and appropriate clamps, having the guards down, having the correct speeds and feeds set, dress and protection factors.
c) Machine tools are quicker, generally more accurate, and give a better-quality finish.
d) 140 degrees
2 a) milling machine
b) centre lathe
c) pillar drill
d) When machining metals friction causes the tool and work to heat up. Coolants are used to reduce the heat and reduce wear on the tools.

MACHINE TOOLS FOR WOOD

A
1 d   2 b   3 c
4 a   5 a

B
1 You will be very unlikely to use a circular saw or band saw in the school workshop.
2 Circular saws and band saws are mainly used by trained teachers and technicians.
3 When using wood machines goggles should be worn at all times.
4 The dust from wood machining operations is a health hazard especially when using manufactured boards.
5 Extreme caution must be taken when using wood machine tools to reduce the risk of serious accidents and dust inhalation.

C
1 a) Consistent quality, quicker, more accurate, can store the program.
b) Cost of the CNC machine could be too high to justify

buying for the task, have to understand programming.
c) Wear dust mask, ensure adequate ventilation, make sure that the guards are closed, make sure that the machine is programmed correctly.
2 a) bandsaw, routing machine, CNC routing machine, electrical jig saw.
b) The size of job to be made, whether it is too dangerous to cut the cams on a band saw due to their size, the quality of the finish required, the number of cams to be made, whether the operator is trained to use the machines.
c) Unlike MDF, softwood timber has a directional grain structure. Differences in finish might occur when machining across or in line with the grain.

REFORMING METALS

A
1 b   2 c   3 b
4 a   5 c

B
1 a)

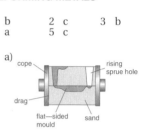

b) Cast iron, bronze, brass, steel, aluminium.

Advantages of Sand Casting	Disadvantages of Sand Casting
Low-cost method	Not as accurate as die casting
Cost effective	Needs finishing
Pattern can be re-used	A mould needs to be made for each product

d) Risers allow the air to be pushed out of the mould cavity, make cast less porous, make sure that mould cavity completely fills up with the metal. Also provides excess metal to allow for contraction on cooling.

C
1 a) Aluminium or other similar answer.
b) Good-quality finish, suitable for large production runs, little finishing is required.
c) Children's toys, car door handles, parts for kitchen equipment, gear box casings.
d)

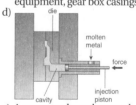

2 a) A process where the metal changes its state during the process e.g. melting.
b) Permanent – gravity die casting, low-pressure die casting, high-pressure die casting. Temporary – sand casting, investment (lost wax process).
c) A wax model of the jewellery piece is made out of wax by carving and shaping. The wax model is coated with a ceramic casing that produces a hard casing

around the wax mould. The wax is then melted out leaving the ceramic shell. The metal for the jewellery piece is melted and poured into the mould. When set the ceramic casing is broken off to leave the metal casting.

REFORMING PLASTICS

A
1 c   2 d   3 b
4 c   5 a

B
1 a)

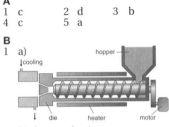

b) thermoplastics
c) polystyrene, polyethylene, nylon
d) window frames, curtain rails – or other similar

C
1 a)

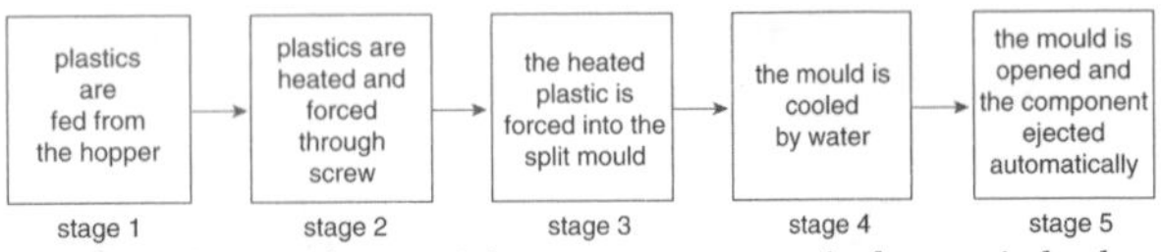

stage 1	stage 2	stage 3	stage 4	stage 5
plastics are fed from the hopper	plastics are heated and forced through screw	the heated plastic is forced into the split mould	the mould is cooled by water	the mould is opened and the component ejected automatically

b) Good-quality product, quick process, cheap to produce, little finishing required, continuous process.
c) thermoplastic
d) The cost of the machine and tools are high. Therefore large batches are required to recoup the cost of the machines and labour.
2 a) Thermosetting plastics require a definite curing stage in the moulding cycle. Injection moulding is a continuous process where the plastic is pushed through the mould at a constant rate. Curing would continuously occur before the product was actually moulded.
b) Is a quick process, high-quality products can be made, a low waste process.
c) Urea-formaldehyde, melamine-formaldehyde.

DEFORMING WOOD, METALS AND PLASTICS

A
1 c   2 b   3 d
4 c   5 a

B 1

Material	Description of Deforming Method
Metal	Deforming around a former or jig. Bending jig can be used.
Plastics	Deforming using line bending, marking out, care to align line over bending slot 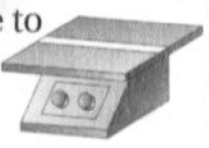
Wood	Can be deformed after lamination where strips of wood are glued together and then bent using formers. 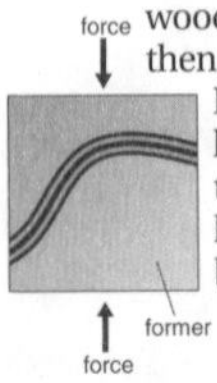 Pressure is first applied so layers are well bonded together. Once former has been made it can be used many times.

C
1 a) Polyethylene

---

b)

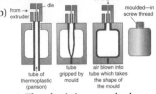

c) The plastic is not melted, so there is no waste in the process.
2 a) Is a quick method, moulds are easy to make, can be used with a variety of coloured sheets, can produce an accurate, good-quality product.
b) Thermoplastic.
c) An accurate mould of the package is made. This needs to have draft angles and be finished to a high standard. The mould is put into the centre of the vacuum forming machine and the plastic sheet placed and clamped into position. The sheet is then heated by the heater until it is pliable. The vacuum is then switched on to pull the pliable sheet around the mould. Once cooled the mould can be taken out of the machine and the plastic shape removed from the mould.

PERMANENT JOINTING OF METALS AND PLASTICS

A
1 b   2 a   3 d
4 a   5 d

B
1

P	A	E	N	K	U	T	P	A	P
A	W	R	D	N	L	O	O	D	A	L
N	R	D	O	U	A	P	M	L	E	A
M	O	X	W	S	F	S	F	A	G	T
G	A	T	E	R	L	A	L	L	N	E
E	D	I	S	E	A	N	O	G	A	S
S	X	N	E	T	N	R	I	I	T
J	A	L	T	N	J	L	O	R	O	A
P	Y	L	A	U	I	C	Q	U	N	N
L	S	N	R	O	U	D	S	S	N	A
N	P	O	L	C	E	T	R	O	B	O

2 a) Hard solders are alloys of copper and zinc.
b) Tensol 12 is a common type of acrylic adhesive.
c) Permanent joints cannot be taken apart.
d) Steel structures are often joined together using arc welding.
e) Care must be taken when riveting plastics to prevent the material from cracking.
f) Soft solders are alloys of tin and lead.
3 The joint is cleaned with a file or emery cloth. A flux is applied to prevent oxidation. The joint is heated using a soldering iron. Solder is applied to the joint.

C
1 a) Brazing can be achieved using school brazing torch, quick method of jointing, reasonably strong.
b)

measure and cut bars to length → use former to bend bars → assemble bars and secure with wire → braze joints together clean up joints → clean up joints → paint rack

---

c) Clean up carefully with file and emery cloth, apply adequate flux, heat up to the correct temperature, apply correct brazing rod.
d) Arc welding, gas welding, adhesives, silver soldering.
2 a) Silver soldering, brazing, soft soldering.
b) The joint area needs to be cleaned up with a file and emery cloth to give a good, clean joining surface. Flux is then applied to the joint. The joint needs to be heated to the correct temperature in such a way that the flame does not allow the surface to oxidise. The brazing rod or solder can then be introduced to the joint.
c) Arc welding, gas welding, riveting.

PERMANENT JOINTING OF WOOD

A
1 c   2 d   3 b
4 a   5 c

B
1 a) true   b) false   c) false
   d) true   e) true
2 a) mortise and tenon
b)

c) mortise chisel
d) The joint would be weak because the mortise has been cut across the grain.

C
1 a) Dowels are used to make the joints more secure and stronger, to help locate parts.
b) The joints would be marked off using templates. A jig would be used to align up dowel holes. Two holes would be drilled. Dowels would be inserted and the joint glued and assembled. 
c) Using jigs and flow production method would speed up the process.
d) This method is quicker, does not rely on skilled labour, can be used for knock-down furniture.
2 a) 45 degree mitre joint.
b) The mitre joint would be cut with the aid of a mitre jig. Glue would be appropriately applied to the joint before clamping. The joints could then be clamped together in a mitre clamp jig. Staples or dowels could be used to strengthen up the joint.
c) Butt joints or housing joints.

TEMPORARY FASTENING METHODS

A
1 c   2 d   3 a
4 b   5 d

B
1

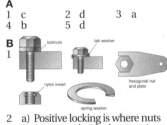

2 a) Positive locking is where nuts are secured with plates or pins.
b) Examples of frictional locking devices are spring washers.
c) Locking devices can be either positive or frictional.
d) Locking devices are often used to prevent parts working loose due to vibration.

3

Positive Locking Devices	Frictional Locking Devices
Hexagonal nut drilled for a split pin to hold the nut and bolt together	Locknuts
Castled nut with split pin	Nylon inserts in nut
Tab washer	Spring washer
Hexagonal nut and plate	

C
1 a)

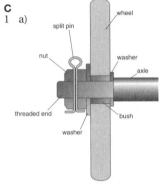

b) Diagram above shows nylon insert in nut. This is a temporary fastening method which would allow wheel to be removed as necessary.
c) Might have to change the wheels, might require oiling.
2 a) Often parts have to be taken apart for inspection, maintenance or to change batteries, etc. A temporary locking method allows the locking method to be undone or released and the product taken apart. The parts can then be put back together once the process has been carried out.
b) Caphead screw, set screw and locknut, nut and bolt, self-tapping screw, socket screw.

KNOCK-DOWN FITTINGS

A
1 c   2 c   3 b
4 a   5 d

B
1 a) Stopped housing joint and modesty bloc.
b)

	Stopped housing joint	
Advantages	1 Good appearance	
	2 Strong joint	
Disadvantages	1 Long time to make	
	2 Have to consider grain	
	Modesty bloc	
Advantages	1 Quick to join	
	2 Can be used with manufactured boards	
Disadvantages	1 Not traditional form of joint	
	2 May not be strong enough for certain types of unit, poor appearance	

C
1 a) bloc fitting
b)

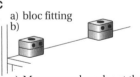

c) Measure and mark out the positions for the bloc. Drill pilot holes. Locate fittings. Screw in place. Adjust if necessary.
2 a) Scan fittings, disc and peg fittings, bloc fittings, modesty bloc fittings.
b) Removes the need to make traditional joints such as

housing joints. This saves time and the knock-down fitting can be fitted by unskilled people. Knock-down fittings are quick to put together and are particularly good for flat pack furniture.

c) Small adjustment screws on some types of knock-down fittings allow adjustments to be made. These are normally made using a screwdriver.

ASSEMBLY AND FITTING

A
1 c   2 c   3 a
4 b   5 c

B
1 a)

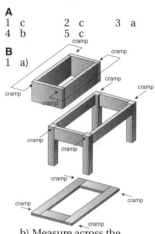

b) Measure across the diagonals, use a try square to check the squareness, put on flat table to check flatness.

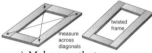

c) Make sure that cramps are square, that there is not an excess of glue, that scrap wood has been used in between the cramp and the wood to prevent bruising, that the correct tension has been used.

C
1 a) The internal thread is cut first because dies are adjustable and taps are not. A cutting paste is used to aid the cutting operation.
   b) For the external threads, the dies are opened to their maximum size by adjusting the screws in the die stock.
   c) After cutting the thread it can be tested in the tapped hole. If the thread is too tight the die-stock screws can be adjusted to reduce the diameter of the die. A second cut can then be taken.
2 a) So that the dowel will revolve correctly when operating.
   b) Make sure that the corners of the housing are cleaned out, apply glue to the joints and fit pieces together, put dowel through the holes and adjust the frame to ensure that the dowel moves freely in the holes, place a packing piece at the free end to prevent the sides from closing in, wipe away excess glue, remove the dowel rod and clamp together, once the glue is dry take away packing piece and clean up frame.
   c) Drill clearance holes in the frame for the dowel shaft.

FINISHING PROCESSES FOR WOOD

A
1 c   2 b   3 a
4 c   5 b

B
1

Product	Type of Finish	Two Reasons for Use
	Paint	Quick, can have different colours
	Creosote	Cheap, quick
	Polyurethane varnish	Hard-wearing, non-toxic, good finish
	French polish	Good-quality finish, seals the grain

C
1 Answer will depend upon the type of finish used. This one is for paint. Clean up the surface of the wood with successively finer glass papers. Seal wood with primer. Use glass paper to smooth down. Spray with undercoat and smooth with glass paper. Use two coats of primer. Spray and smooth with 3 to 4 layers of cellulose paint.
2 a) Teak or iroko.
   b) Wood would be carefully sanded down using glass papers. A coarser grit size would be used first and the product sanded down with finer grit papers. The glass paper would be wrapped around a sanding block. The varnish would be applied with a brush or cloth and rubbed down with a fine glass paper in between coats.
   c) Spraying, soaking in tanks, forcing the preservative into the wood under pressure.

FINISHING PROCESSES FOR METAL AND PLASTICS

A
1 b   2 a   3 d
4 c   5 b

B
1 Your answer should include a neat sketch. Wire joints are cleaned up with a file and emery cloth. Joints are filed to as near the size of the wire as possible. Plastics coating machine switched on to fluidise the bed. Crate is heated up to about 120 degrees centigrade. Metal dipped into fluidised plastics to coat.

C 1

Suitable Finish	Safety Precautions
Enamelling	Heat protective gloves and goggles. Tongs to pick up metal. Care with acid tank.
Chrome plating	Goggles and protective clothing to be worn.
Paints	Use in well-ventilated room or spray booth with extractor fan.

2 a) Paint.
   b) The surface should be thoroughly degreased and cleaned. The surface can then be rubbed down with wet and dry paper to get a smooth finish. The metal surface is firstly sprayed with a primer layer of paint. This is smoothed down with wet and dry paper. A paint undercoat is then applied and left to dry. Once dry, successive layers of the required colour can be applied until a good finish has been achieved. The layers of paint should be smoothed down with wet and dry paper between each coat. The spraying should be done in a well-ventilated room. A mask and eye protection should be worn.

CNC IN MANUFACTURING

A
1 c   2 c   3 a
4 d   5 c

B
1

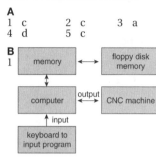

2 feed rate
  depth of cut
  type of cutter
  type of material

C
1 a) Answers could include: size of the job, if it can be clamped correctly in the machine, the cost of the job, machining speed.
   b) Answers could include: quicker, more accurate, consistent housing size, higher-quality product, less skill needed.
   c) Answers could include: make use of guards, should be adequate ventilation, correct speeds and feeds should be used, job needs to be clamped down properly.
2 a) Produces accurate label shapes, can machine complex shapes easily, produces a good surface finish, can machine at a rapid rate, can produce identical labels, does not require the use of specialist jigs or fixtures.
   b) Must use the correct cutting speed, use the correct feed rate, make sure that the depth of cut is correct.

TESTING FOR QUALITY

A
1 b   2 c   3 a
4 c   5 c

B
1 a)

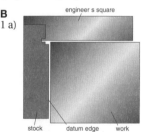

b) Ensure tools not dropped, kept clean, dirt wiped from their faces, checked regularly for accuracy.

C
1 a)

b) Possible tools are: micrometer, vernier, callipers.

---

c) Micrometer will measure smallest dimension, vernier next smallest and callipers largest dimension.
2 a) external callipers and rule or a micrometer.
   b) micrometer
   c) vernier calliper or 50-75 mm micrometer
   d) An engineer's try square would be used. Place the stock of the try square against the datum face and use the square to check whether the two sides are at right angles.
   e) Clean any metal burrs off with a file or emery cloth, clean the tool to get rid of any grease or dirt.

INDUSTRIAL APPLICATIONS

TYPES OF PRODUCTION

A
1 b   2 a   3 b
4 c   5 c

B
1 a) false   b) true   c) true
  d) false   e) true
2 a) In-line production is mainly used for the mass production of products such as cars, washing machines and fridges.
   b) Semiskilled operators tend to be used during in-line production.
   c) In-line production is very expensive to set up and thousands of products have to be made to make a profit.
   d) In-line production is difficult to plan and breakdowns are costly.

C
1 a) Answers to include: quicker, more accurate, semiskilled operators can be used, uniform products.
   b) Answers to include: no need to make the expensive jig and tools, can be easily reprogrammed for different uses.
   c) Show your design to your teacher.
2 a) To speed up production, to minimise mistakes, to standardise quality, so that semiskilled workers can be used.
   b) CNC machines can accurately position tools on work, the machines produce parts at high speed, CNC machines can assure the quality of the product.
   c) Machine flexibility refers to how quickly a machine can be changed to make a new product or different number of components.

COMMERCIAL SYSTEMS

A
1 b   2 a   3 c
4 d   5 d

B
1 a) weld and spray
  b) respond quickly
  c) team-working cells
  d) batch production
2 a) false   b) true
  c) true   d) true

C
1 a) Just-in-time manufacture – where products are bought in or made in the right quantities and at the right time for manufacture.

b) Include: keeps stocks down, keeps the workplace tidier, keeps costs down throughout the company.

c) Include: possibility of products not reaching production stages on time, reliant on quality standards of suppliers, reduces choice of suppliers.

d) Supermarkets make use of JIT by using point of sale systems. When goods go through the system the infra-red scanner notes the type of goods sold. This information is fed back to the warehouse to order more stock.

2 a) Concurrent manufacture is where all aspects of design and manufacture are thoroughly considered at the design stage. This includes how it will be made, what sales are required and how the product will be developed. All departments in the company are therefore involved in design decisions.

b) It is a quicker process, makes sure that there are no problems in the latter manufacturing stages and that the product can be made, reduces the number of unwanted goods that cannot be sold.

BATCH PRODUCTION

A
1 c   2 a   3 a
4 c   5 b

B
1 a) guides   b) clamped
c) drilling   d) milling

2 Answers could include: a method of quickly locating component, foolproof so component can only be located correct way round, method of positioning tools accurately, allow guards to be used properly, allow swarf, wood or plastics cuttings to be cleaned quickly after each operation, allow components to seat properly in jig or fixture.

C
1 a)

CNC Costs	Jigs and Fixtures Costs
Cost of initial programming	Cost of making jigs and fixtures
Material costs	Material costs
Overhead costs	Overhead costs
Supervisor costs	Operator costs
Running costs	Running costs
Cost of changing program	Costs of setting up machine

b) Speed up production process, clamp workpiece into place so measuring and marking out does not need to be carried out, guides tools for machining.

c) Gantt chart indicates sequence of operations and time they will take.

2 a) To speed up production, to easily locate the products

on the machine, to ensure the same dimensions are machined time and time again, can be used with semiskilled personnel, to keep the same quality conditions for each product.

b) Cost of making the fixture, material costs, cost of the operator (labour costs), cost of electricity and running the machine, cost of fitting the fixture to the machine, overhead costs.

c) The cost of making the fixture in the first place is expensive and you would not recoup the cost of the fixture on just one component.

USE OF STANDARD COMPONENTS

A
1 c   2 c   3 a
4 c   5 a

B
1 Answers to include: more reliable, cheaper, can control quality of supplier, no need for expensive equipment.

2 a) Answers could include: bearings, gears, nuts and bolts, pulleys, round bars, dowels.

b) Answers could include: bearings might be used on a bicycle wheel, gears in an electric drill.

C
1 a)

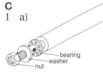

split pin
bearing
washer
nut

b) From suppliers' catalogues, or from computer databases.

c) Cost, availability, quality, how many were needed.

2 a) Examples include nuts and bolts, bearings, washers, brake cables, set screws, bushes, gears, sprockets, chains, etc.

b) Do not have to make them themselves therefore generally cheaper, usually good quality, parts tend to

be reliable, do not need all the machines and people required for manufacture.

c) Do not need to hold large stocks of parts, can order different parts if models change, reduces the way in which large amounts of unwanted stocks may be left at the end of a production run.

USE OF CAD/CAM IN INDUSTRY

A
1 d   2 c   3 a
4 a   5 a

B
1

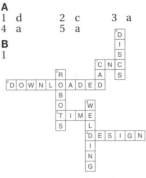

2 Design process speeded up, allows solid modelling of product, enables design changes to be made quickly, information can be stored easily on disk, data can be easily transmitted to other design and manufacturing areas,

3 a) computer-controlled
b) new sequence
c) gripping devices
d) welding

C
1 Show your answers for this to your teacher.

2 a) CAD solid modelling is where components are drawn and designed using 3-D solid modelling packages on computer screens. Models can be coloured and rotated to help visualise the design in full.

b) Can be reprogrammed easily for different batch sizes, can work more continuously than people, gives constant quality levels, can be linked up with design computer, can be linked to a factory-wide computer system, can be used in hazardous conditions.

c) Answers include: hard disks, floppy disks, smart cards, CD-ROMs.

COMPUTER INTEGRATED SYSTEMS

A
1 d   2 b   3 a
4 b   5 d

B
1 false   2 true   3 true
4 false   5 true   6 true

C
1 a) computer integrated manufacture

b) Answers could include: can integrate the factory, can have CAD quickly downloaded, production can be constantly monitored, companies can have effective links with suppliers, can produce data on many aspects of production plant.

c) Answers could include: expensive to install, not all companies can afford it, breakdowns are expensive, difficult to maintain.

2 a) Computer-aided machines, computer-aided design areas, maintenance areas, production control, sales area, stock control, warehousing.

b) Expensive to install, complicated to run, costly if they break down, may not require one due to the small volume of goods produced.

c)

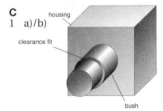

CONTROLLING THE QUALITY

A
1 c   2 d   3 a
4 c   5 a

B
1 a) 100% inspection is where inspection is carried out on the whole of the batch.

b) Variable – a characteristic that can be measured, lies between a range of values. Attributes – not measurable quantities but are yes or no decisions.

c) Tolerance – sum of high and low limits of a measurement.

C
1 a)/b)

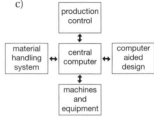

housing
clearance fit
bush

Clearance fit where shaft can rotate freely in hole (for example, whirly gig washing lines). Interference fit where shaft is larger than hole (for example, location dowels in jigs and fixtures).

c)

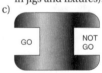

GO   NOT GO

gap gauge

2 a) 25.2 mm
b) 25.0 mm
c) tolerance = upper limit – lower limit
d) tolerance = 0.2 mm
e) The shaft would not go into the hole.
g) A gap gauge.

LETTS EDUCATIONAL
The Chiswick Centre
414 Chiswick High Road
London W4 5TF
Tel: 020 8996 3333
Fax: 020 8742 8390
Email: mail@lettsed.co.uk
Website: www.letts-education.com

These are GCSE-style questions. Answer all parts of the questions.

1 The grooves on a book rack are to be manufactured using a CNC wood routing machine.

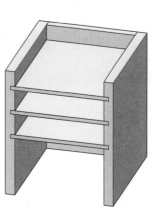

a) Give three advantages of using the CNC routing machine for the operation.

....

....

.... **(3 marks)**

b) Give one disadvantage of using the CNC method rather than making the grooves by hand.

.... **(1 mark)**

c) State three safety precautions that have to be observed when machining the wood on the CNC routing machine.

....

....

.... **(3 marks)**

2 A number of identically shaped cams for a move-along toy have to be cut out accurately.

a) Name two types of machine tools that could be used for the job.

....

.... **(2 marks)**

b) What factors would you consider before selecting a particular machine for the job?

....

.... **(2 marks)**

c) What machining problems might occur if you were using softwood timber rather than MDF for the task?

....

.... **(2 marks)**

Score   / 13

How well did you do?

0–5 correct	Try again
6–14 correct	Getting there
15–18 correct	Good work
19–23 correct	Excellent!

TOTAL SCORE   / 23

For more information on this topic see pages 48–49 of your Success Guide

REFORMING METALS

A

A

Choose just one answer, a, b, c or d.

1 Which of the following is not a process used in the manufacture of metals?
a) investment casting
b) vacuum forming
c) high-pressure die casting
d) sand casting   (1 mark)

2 Which of the following metals is usually used in high-pressure die casting?
a) cast iron
b) high speed steel
c) aluminium alloy
d) titanium alloy   (1 mark)

3 Investment casting is also known as:
a) sand casting   b) lost wax casting
c) die casting   d) steel casting   (1 mark)

4 Which of the following manufacturing processes is a temporary casting process?
a) sand casting
b) low-pressure die casting
c) high-pressure die casting
d) gravity die casting   (1 mark)

5 A metal reforming process is one where the:
a) metal is machined and forms swarf as waste
b) process is carried out at temperatures greater than 1 500 degrees centigrade
c) metal changes its state during the process
d) process is carried out at temperatures less than 50 degrees centigrade   (1 mark)

Score   / 5

B

Answer all parts of the questions.

1 a) The diagram below shows a cross-section through a sand casting.

Label the following parts on the diagram

– cope, drag, sand, mould, rising sprue hole.

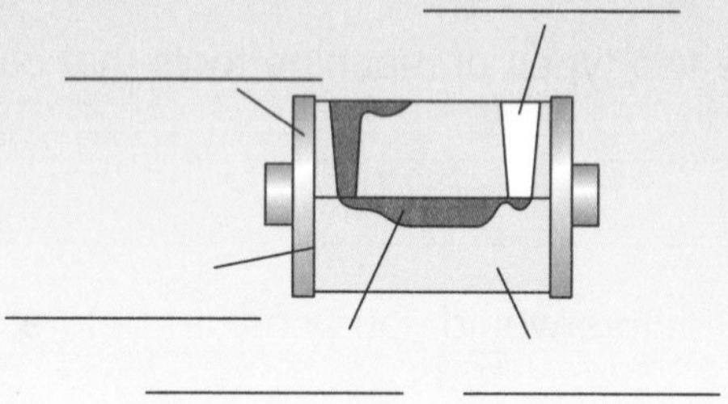

(5 marks)

b) State the name of one type of metal that is often cast using this process.

.... (1 mark)

c) Give three advantages and three disadvantages of the sand casting process. Complete the table below.

Advantages of Sand Casting	Disadvantages of Sand Casting

(6 marks)

d) What is the purpose of the risers in the process?

.... (1 mark)

Score   / 13

C These are GCSE-style questions. Answer all parts of the questions.

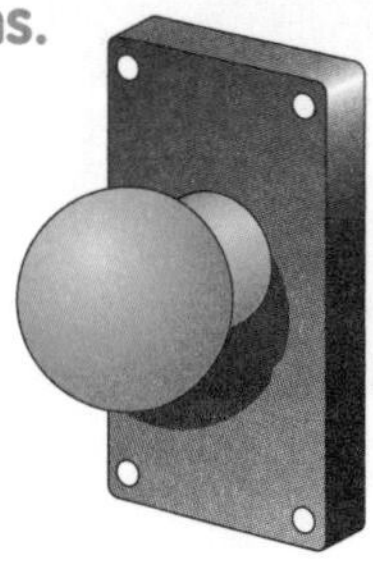

1 The diagram shows a die cast door knob that has been bought for a bathroom cabinet.

a) Suggest a material that could be used for the door knob.

.... (1 mark)

b) Give two reasons why die casting is a suitable process for the manufacture of the door knobs.

....

.... (2 marks)

c) Name three other products that are often made by die casting.

....

....

.... (3 marks)

d) Label the diagram showing the main parts of a die casting machine.

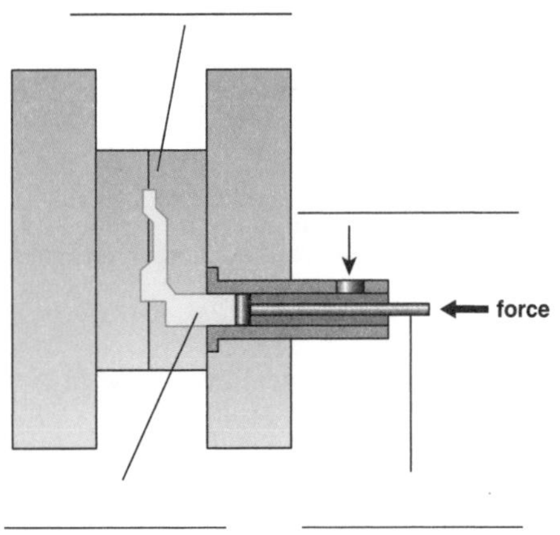

(4 marks)

2 a) What is meant by reforming?

.... (1 mark)

b) Name one permanent reforming method and one temporary reforming method.

....

.... (2 marks)

c) Briefly explain how investment casting can be used to make intricate jewellery items.

....

....

....

.... (4 marks)

Score   / 17

How well did you do?

0–11 correct   Try again
12–20 correct   Getting there
21–28 correct   Good work
29–35 correct   Excellent!

TOTAL SCORE   / 35

For more information on this topic
see pages 50–51 of your Success Guide

REFORMING PLASTICS

Choose just one answer, a, b, c or d.

1 Which of the following is not a process used in the manufacture of plastics?
a) extrusion moulding
b) compression moulding
c) die casting   d) monomer casting   (1 mark)

2 Which of the following processes is used for the production of thermosetting plastics?
a) injection moulding   b) plastics extrusion
c) vacuum forming
d) compression moulding   (1 mark)

3 In which of the following processes would you pour the plastics into an open mould?
a) compression moulding
b) monomer casting
c) extrusion
d) injection moulding   (1 mark)

4 Which of the following products would you expect to be made using plastics extrusion?
a) plastic kettle bodies
b) plastic cups
c) plastic curtain rails
d) kitchen cupboard door knobs   (1 mark)

5 Which of the following processes includes a time for curing the plastics during moulding?
a) compression moulding
b) injection moulding
c) plastics extrusion moulding
d) vacuum forming   (1 mark)

Score   / 5

B

Answer all parts of the question.

1 The diagram below shows a cross-sectional view of a plastics extrusion moulding machine.

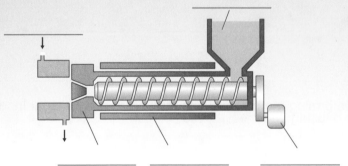

a) Label the parts shown on the diagram.   (5 marks)

b) State whether the extrusion moulder should be used for thermoplastics or thermosetting plastics.
.... (1 mark)

c) Give one example of a type of plastic that may be made using the extrusion moulding machine.
.... (1 mark)

d) Give two examples of products that are often made using extrusion.
....
.... (2 marks)

Score   / 9

C **These are GCSE-style questions. Answer all parts of the questions.**

1 The diagram shows a small toy that is to be made using injection moulding.

a) Complete the flow diagram below showing the main stages of the moulding process.

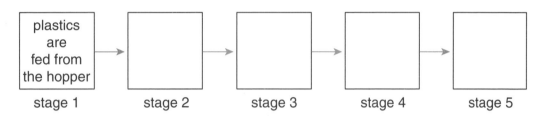

plastics are fed from the hopper				
stage 1	stage 2	stage 3	stage 4	stage 5

(4 marks)

b) Give two advantages of using injection moulding for the production of plastics goods.

....

.... (2 marks)

c) State whether injection moulding is used for making thermosetting or thermoplastic products.

.... (1 mark)

d) Briefly explain why injection moulding may not be suitable for small batches of products.

....

....

.... (3 marks)

2 **a)** Explain why injection moulding is not used for thermosetting plastics.

....

.... (2 marks)

b) Give three advantages of using compression moulding to make products.

....

....

.... (3 marks)

c) State one type of plastics which is often moulded using the compression moulding process.

.... (1 mark)

Score   / 16

How well did you do?

0–7 correct   Try again
8–16 correct   Getting there
17–22 correct   Good work
23–30 correct   Excellent!

TOTAL SCORE   / 30

For more information on this topic see pages 52–53 of your Success Guide

DEFORMING WOOD, METALS AND PLASTICS

A Choose just one answer, a, b, c or d.

1 Which of the following is not a deforming process?
  a) wood laminating **b)** blow moulding
  c) plastics extrusion **d)** vacuum forming
  (1 mark)

2 Which of the following products is often made using blow moulding?
  a) screwdriver handles
  b) plastic milk containers
  c) CD cases **d)** computer casings
  (1 mark)

3 Which of the following processes could be used for the manufacture of plastic margarine tubs?
  a) sand casting **b)** plastics extrusion
  c) compression moulding
  d) vacuum forming (1 mark)

4 Car body panels are likely to be made by:
  a) laminating
  b) blow moulding
  c) metal pressing
  d) die casting (1 mark)

5 Blow moulding operations are carried out on:
  a) thermoplastics
  b) thermosetting plastics
  c) bakelite
  d) aluminium alloys (1 mark)

Score / 5

B Answer all parts of the question.

1 A small number of hooks are to be made so that tools can be hung up in a garden shed.

The hooks are to be made in one piece and can be made from either wood, metal or plastics.

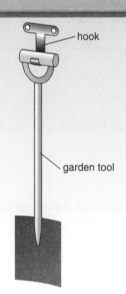

hook

garden tool

For each material briefly describe a deforming method that could be used to make the hooks.

Material	Description of Deforming Method
Metal	
Plastics	
Wood	

(9 marks)

Score / 9

C

These are GCSE-style questions. Answer all parts of the questions.

1 The drinks bottle shown is manufactured by blow moulding.

a) Name a common type of thermoplastic that blow-moulded bottles are often made from.

.... (1 mark)

b) Using neat sketches describe the blow moulding process.

(6 marks)

c) Briefly explain why blow moulding is an example of a deforming process.

....

.... (2 marks)

2 A small package for an electronic product is to be made by vacuum forming.

a) Give two reasons why vacuum forming is suitable.

....

.... (2 marks)

b) State whether a thermoplastic or thermosetting plastic would be used.

.... (1 mark)

c) Briefly explain the stages of the vacuum forming process.

....

....

....

.... (4 marks)

Score / 16

How well did you do?

0–7 correct Try again
8–16 correct Getting there
17–22 correct Good work
23–30 correct Excellent!

TOTAL SCORE / 30

For more information on this topic see pages 54–55 of your Success Guide

PERMANENT JOINTING OF METALS AND PLASTICS

A Choose just one answer, a, b, c or d.

1 Which of the following is not a permanent method of jointing?
a) brazing
b) nuts and bolts
c) riveting
d) soft soldering   (1 mark)

2 Soft soldering is a jointing method that can be used to join:
a) brass   b) stainless steel
c) cast iron   d) nylon   (1 mark)

3 Soft solder is an alloy of:
a) tin and brass
b) brass and aluminium
c) tin and aluminium
d) tin and lead   (1 mark)

4 Plastics are often joined using:
a) a hot air gun
b) electric arc welding machine
c) oxyacetylene welding
d) soldering   (1 mark)

5 When soldering and brazing, oxidation is prevented by using a suitable type of:
a) flax
b) flex
c) flocculent
d) flux   (1 mark)

Score   / 5

B Answer all parts of the questions.

1 Find the following types of rivets in the word search.
pop, snap, round, flat, pan, countersunk

P	A	E	N	K	U	T	R	P	A	P
A	W	R	D	N	L	U	O	D	A	L
N	R	D	O	U	A	P	M	L	E	A
M	O	X	W	S	F	S	F	A	G	T
G	A	T	E	R	L	A	J	L	N	E
E	D	I	S	E	A	N	O	O	A	S
S	N	N	P	T	N	R	I	I	I	T
U	A	L	T	N	J	I	O	P	O	A
P	T	L	A	U	I	C	O	U	N	N
L	S	N	R	O	U	D	S	S	N	A
N	P	O	L	C	E	T	R	O	E	D

(6 marks)

2 Use these phrases to complete the sentences.

| arc welding | acrylic adhesive | cracking | hard solders | soft solders | permanent joints |

a) .... are alloys of copper and zinc.

b) Tensol 12 is a common type of ....

c) .... cannot be taken apart.

d) Steel structures are often joined together using ....

e) Care must be taken when riveting plastics to prevent the material from ....

f) .... are alloys of tin and lead.   (6 marks)

3 These sentences describe the sequence for ensuring a good soft-soldered joint. Read the sentences and put them in their correct order.

Solder is applied to the joint.   ☐

A flux is applied to prevent oxidation.   ☐

The joint is heated using a soldering iron.   ☐

The joint is cleaned with a file or emery cloth.   ☐

(4 marks)

Score   / 16

These are GCSE-style questions. Answer all parts of the questions.

1 A small rack is to be made in your school workshop using 6 mm diameter mild steel bar.

a) Give two reasons why brazing would be a convenient method to make the joints.

....

.... (2 marks)

b) Use a flow chart to describe the stages necessary to produce the rack.

(6 marks)

c) Give two precautions that should be taken to ensure good, strong joints.

....

.... (2 marks)

d) State two other methods that could be used to make the joints for the rack.

....

.... (2 marks)

2 a) Name a suitable heat jointing method that can be used to permanently join copper parts together.

.... (1 mark)

b) Explain how you would produce a good joint when using the process.

....

....

.... (3 marks)

c) What methods would be suitable for making stronger joints for steel structures?

....

.... (2 marks)

Score   / 18

How well did you do?

0–13 correct	Try again
14–25 correct	Getting there
26–33 correct	Good work
34–39 correct	Excellent!

TOTAL SCORE   / 39

For more information on this topic see pages 56–57 of your Success Guide

PERMANENT JOINTING OF WOOD

A Choose just one answer a, b, c or d

1 The simplest form of joint is a:
a) dovetail joint   b) housing joint
c) butt joint   d) finger joint   (1 mark)

2 Which of the following is not a joint used to join natural timbers?
a) mortise and tenon
b) stopped housing
c) comb joint
d) silver soldered   (1 mark)

3 Mitre joints are often used to produce the corners of:
a) cricket bats
b) picture frames
c) wooden chairs
d) expensive furniture   (1 mark)

4 Butt joints are often reinforced using:
a) wooden dowels
b) pop rivets
c) wooden wedges
d) nuts and bolts   (1 mark)

5 The mitre angle of a mitred joint is:
a) 30 degrees
b) 50 degrees
c) 45 degrees
d) 40 degrees   (1 mark)

Score   / 5

B Answer all parts of the questions.

1 State whether these statements are true or false.

	True	False
a) Knock-down fittings tend to be used for jointing manufactured wood.	☐	☐
b) Dovetail joints are generally weaker than butt joints.	☐	☐
c) Housing joints are not used for shelf constructions.	☐	☐
d) A comb joint is also called a finger joint.	☐	☐
e) Comb joints are often used to construct the corners of small boxes.	☐	☐

(5 marks)

2 The diagram below shows a corner joint for part of a stool construction.

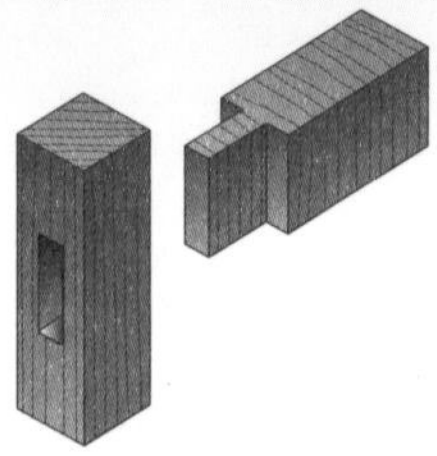

a) Name the type of joint shown.

....   (1 mark)

b) On the diagram shown label the mortise and the tenon.   (2 marks)

c) What tool would be used to cut the mortise?

....   (1 mark)

d) What would be a major problem if the joint was made in the way shown in the diagram?

....   (2 marks)

Score   / 11

C **These are GCSE-style questions. Answer all parts of the questions.**

1 A small batch of thirty coffee tables is going to be made in a school workshop. It has been decided that butt joints will be used for the corners indicated in the diagram.

a) State why the dowels have been used in the manufacture of each joint.

....

.... (2 marks)

b) Explain the steps that would be used to make one of the joints.

....

....

....

.... (5 marks)

c) Explain how the dowelling operation for the total batch of tables could be speeded up.

....

.... (2 marks)

d) Give two advantages of using this method rather than a mortise and tenon method.

....

.... (2 marks)

2 You are to design and make a small picture frame for a school project.

a) What type of joint would be suitable for the frame?

.... (1 mark)

b) Explain how you might ensure that you have an accurate and secure joint after manufacture.

....

....

....

.... (4 marks)

c) Name one other joint that is often used for low-strength applications.

.... (1 mark)

Score   / 17

How well did you do?

0–10 correct   Try again
11–19 correct Getting there
20–25 correct Good work
26–33 correct Excellent!

TOTAL SCORE   / 33

For more information on this topic see pages 58–59 of your Success Guide

TEMPORARY FASTENING METHODS

A Choose just one answer, a, b, c or d.

1 Which of the following are not temporary fastenings?
a) self-tapping screws
b) nuts and bolts
c) pop rivets
d) wood screws   (1 mark)

2 A temporary fastening is often used to:
a) weld parts of cars together
b) glue together the layers of a laminated skate board
c) braze parts of flower hanging basket brackets together
d) bolt and unbolt inspection covers on gear boxes casings   (1 mark)

3 Allen keys are often used to tighten and loosen:
a) caphead screws
b) round-head wood screws
c) hexagonal headed nuts
d) nails   (1 mark)

4 Self-tapping screws are often used to join together:
a) porcelain china parts
b) sheet metal guards on workshop machines
c) girders for railway bridges
d) the panels for garden fences   (1 mark)

5 Which of the following is not a common type of wood screw?
a) round-head   b) cheese head
c) countersunk   d) clamp head (1 mark)

Score   / 5

B Answer all parts of the questions.

1 Using neat diagrams, sketch an example of a positive locking device and a frictional locking device.

(4 marks)

2 Choose one of these phrases to complete the following sentences.

vibration	positive locking	frictional locking devices	frictional

a) .... is where nuts are secured with plates or pins.

b) Examples of .... are spring washers.

c) Locking devices can be either positive or ....

d) Locking devices are often used to prevent parts working loose due to .... (4 marks)

3 Complete the table below. Give three examples of frictional locking devices and three examples of positive locking devices.

Positive Locking Devices	Frictional Locking Devices

(6 marks)

Score   / 14

C **These are GCSE-style questions. Answer all parts of the questions.**

1 You have been asked to attach the wheels to the axle of the baby pram shown in the diagram.

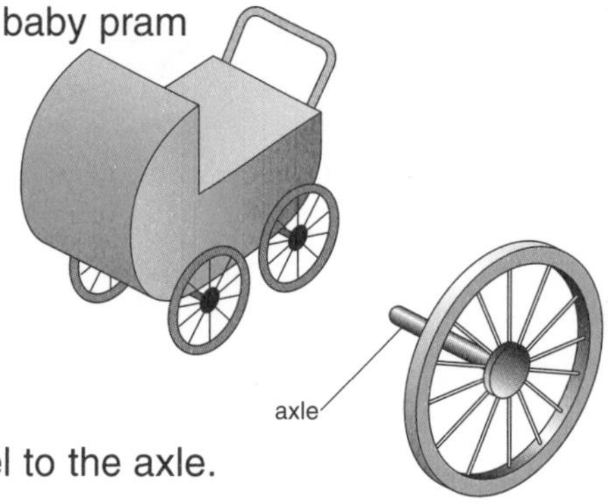

axle

a) Make a neat sketch of your method of attaching the wheel to the axle.

(5 marks)

b) State whether your method is a temporary or a permanent type of fixing.

.... (1 mark)

c) Explain what type of maintenance might be required for the wheel and axle during the life of the pram.

....

....

.... (3 marks)

2 a) Briefly explain why temporary locking devices are often preferred to permanent methods.

....

....

.... (3 marks)

b) Give three examples of temporary locking methods.

....

....

.... (3 marks)

Score   / 15

How well did you do?

0–10 correct   Try again
11–19 correct   Getting there
20–27 correct   Good work
28–34 correct   Excellent!

TOTAL SCORE   **/ 34**

For more information on this topic
see pages 60–61 of your Success Guide

KNOCK-DOWN FITTINGS

A Choose just one answer, a, b, c or d.

1 Knock-down fittings are widely used for joining:
   a) pillar drill machine parts
   b) fishing rod sections
   c) flat-pack furniture
   d) computer keyboard sections   (1 mark)

2 Which of the following is not a type of knock-down fitting?
   a) scan fitting   b) disc and peg fitting
   c) ellipse fitting   d) bloc fitting   (1 mark)

3 Knock-down fittings have been designed to be used mainly with:
   a) natural timbers
   b) manufactured boards
   c) oak panels
   d) hardwood timbers   (1 mark)

4 Which of the following tools is required to align the disc when using disc and peg fittings?
   a) screwdriver
   b) ball pin hammer
   c) open-ended spanner
   d) ring spanner   (1 mark)

5 Bloc-fittings are generally made from:
   a) plywood
   b) brass
   c) aluminium
   d) plastics   (1 mark)

Score   / 5

B Answer all parts of the question.

1 The diagrams below show two possible ways of attaching shelves in a bookcase.

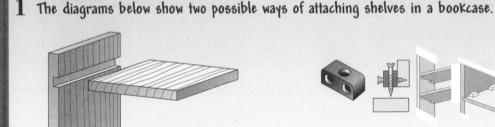
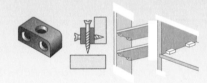

a) Name the types of joints that are used in each case.

....

....   (2 marks)

b) Give two advantages and two disadvantages of each method.

	Method 1	Method 2
Advantages	1	1
	2	2
Disadvantages	1	1
	2	2

(8 marks)

Score   / 10

C **These are GCSE-style questions. Answer all parts of the questions.**

1 Knock-down fittings are used to join together the outside frame of a kitchen wall unit.

This is shown in the diagram.

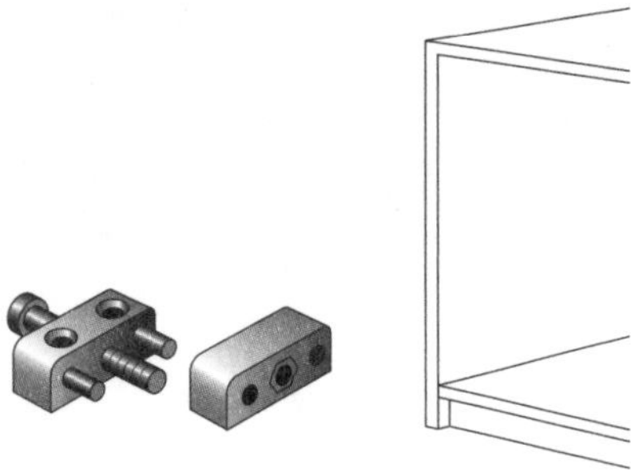

a) Name the type of fitting that is being used.

.... (2 marks)

b) Redraw the fittings to show how they would be located to hold the frame together.

(4 marks)

c) Explain the stages needed to attach the fittings and join the frame together.

....

....

....

.... (4 marks)

2 a) Name three types of knock-down fittings.

....

....

.... (3 marks)

b) Explain the advantages of using knock-down fittings for indoor furniture.

....

....

.... (3 marks)

c) How do some knock-down fittings allow you to make slight adjustments for aligning furniture doors and other parts?

....

.... (2 marks)

Score   / 18

How well did you do?

0–10 correct   Try again
11–19 correct   Getting there
20–25 correct   Good work
26–33 correct   Excellent!

TOTAL SCORE   / 33

For more information on this topic
see pages 62–63 of your Success Guide

ASSEMBLY AND FITTING

Choose just one answer, a, b, c or d.

1 Which of the following is not a general type of wood construction?
a) carcase construction
b) flat frame
c) snap construction
d) stool frame (1 mark)

2 Which of the following tools is often used to help start screws in softwoods?
a) centre punch   b) scriber
c) bradawl   d) chisel (1 mark)

3 Which of the following procedures should be carried out when using screws in hardwoods?
a) drill a pilot hole
b) chisel out a starting groove
c) use a reamer to open up the hole
d) use a countersink drill bit (1 mark)

4 Which of the following is commonly used to clamp together wooden constructions?
a) tool maker's clamps
b) sash cramps
c) pull cramps
d) wood clamps (1 mark)

5 Which of the following are not tools used for metal?
a) tool maker's clamps
b) taps
c) bradawl
d) dies (1 mark)

Score   / 5

B

Answer all parts of the question.

1 The constructions shown below are to be joined together using joints and wood glue.

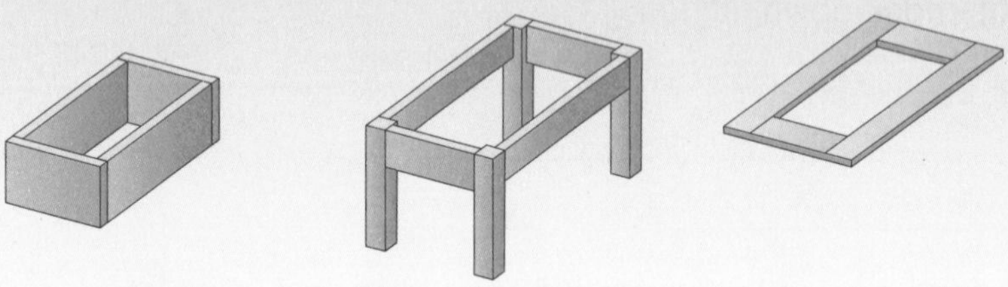

a) Show on each of the diagrams how you would position the cramps during the gluing process. (2 marks)

b) With the aid of sketches, explain two ways in which you could ensure that the frames were flat and square after they had been cramped.

(4 marks)

c) What precautions would you take to ensure that you make a good job of the cramping process?

(3 marks)

Score   / 9

C These are GCSE-style questions. Answer all parts of the questions.

1 The two pieces of a table lamp fitting require joining together with a threaded stud.

With the aid of sketches describe the way in which you would:

a) make the internal thread

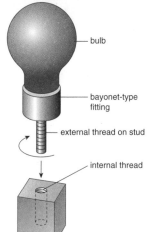
— bulb
— bayonet-type fitting
— external thread on stud
— internal thread

b) make the external thread on the stud

c) fit the two parts together

(9 marks)

2 A framework for a cam toy requires gluing together. The frame for the toy is shown.

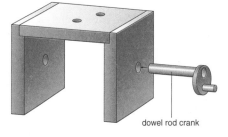
dowel rod crank

a) Why is it important that the sides are glued together so that the sides of the framework are square?

.... (1 mark)

b) Explain the steps you would take to make sure that the frame is squarely glued together.

....

....

....

.... (4 marks)

c) How would you ensure that the dowel rod would turn in the holes when used?

.... (1 mark)

Score   / 15

How well did you do?

0–9 correct	Try again
10–15 correct	Getting there
16–23 correct	Good work
24–29 correct	Excellent!

TOTAL SCORE   / 29

For more information on this topic see pages 64–65 of your Success Guide

FINISHING PROCESSES FOR WOOD

Choose just one answer, a, b, c or d.

1 Which of the following woods has natural protection from its own oils?
a) oak
b) beech
c) teak
d) pine   (1 mark)

2 Which of the following is not a finishing treatment for wood?
a) varnish
b) Brasso
c) bees' wax
d) stain   (1 mark)

3 A common wood preserve for garden fences is:
a) creosote
b) wax polish
c) French polish
d) polyurethane varnish   (1 mark)

4 High-class finishes on furniture can be produced with the aid of a:
a) file
b) rasp
c) cabinet scraper
d) plane   (1 mark)

5 Woods can be coloured using:
a) oils
b) wood stains
c) wax polish
d) clear varnish   (1 mark)

Score   / 5

B

Answer all parts of the question.

1 For each of the products shown give an example of a type of finish you would use.
Give two reasons why you have chosen each of the finishes.

Product	Type of Finish	Two Reasons For Use

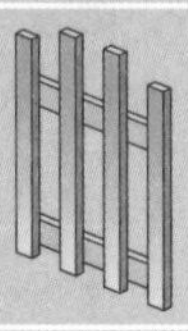		
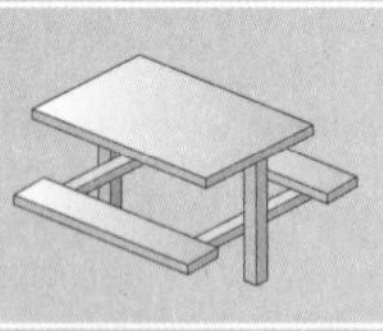		

(8 marks)

Score   / 8

C These are GCSE-style questions. Answer all parts of the questions.

1 The toy train shown requires finishing ready for use.

Describe the processes, tools and materials you would use to produce a good protective finish for the toy.

....

....

....

....

....

....

....

....

....

.... (10 marks)

2 a) Name a type of wood that has some natural protection against weathering.

.... (1 mark)

b) Explain what steps you would take to get a high-quality finish when using polyurethane varnish to finish off wooden products.

....

....

....

.... (3 marks)

c) Name two industrial methods that can be used to impregnate wood with wood preservatives.

....

....

.... (2 marks)

Score   / 16

How well did you do?

0–9 correct   Try again
10–15 correct   Getting there
16–23 correct   Good work
24–29 correct   Excellent!

TOTAL SCORE   / 29

For more information on this topic
see pages 66–67 of your Success Guide

FINISHING PROCESSES FOR METAL AND PLASTICS

A Choose just one answer, a, b, c or d.

1 Electro-plating is often used to:
a) steel plate products
b) chrome plate products
c) iron plate products
d) brass plate products (1 mark)

2 Lacquers are often used on non-ferrous metals to prevent:
a) tarnishing b) melting
c) bending d) cracking (1 mark)

3 In the school workshop, enamelling is often used to produce designs on:
a) hand tools
b) card models
c) plastic brackets
d) jewellery (1 mark)

4 The edge of a plastics product can be cleaned up and smoothed using:
a) grip-filing
b) push-filing
c) draw-filing
d) edge-filing (1 mark)

5 The faces of many metals and plastics can be polished on a:
a) grinding machine
b) buffing machine
c) smoothing machine
d) pillar drill (1 mark)

Score / 5

B Answer all parts of the question.

1 The small milk crate has been made by forming the round bars into shape and then brazing the parts together.

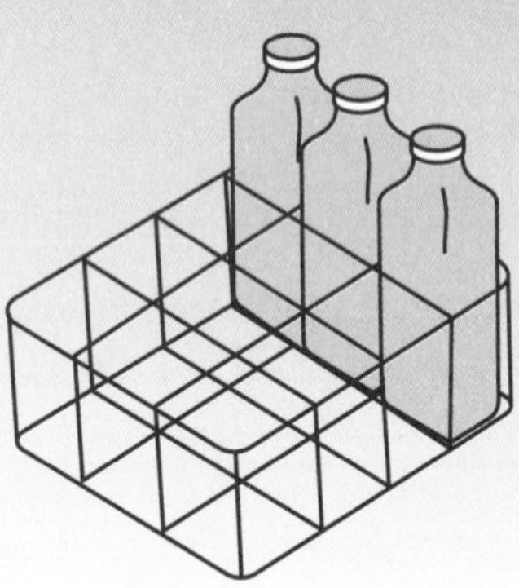

Explain the stages that would have to be carried out to plastic coat the crate in the school workshop.

(8 marks)

Score / 8

68

C **These are GCSE-style questions. Answer all parts of the questions.**

1 The table below shows three products that are in the finishing stage.

Product	Suitable Finish	Safety Precautions

a) For each product, select a suitable finish that could be used. (3 marks)

b) For each product state two safety precautions that should be observed when carrying out the process. (9 marks)

2 The body of a model car is to be coloured by paint spraying.

a) What type of paint would be used to spray the metal?

.... (1 mark)

b) Explain how you would achieve a high-class sprayed finish.

....

....

....

....

.... (3 marks)

c) What safety precautions would you take during the spraying process?

....

....

....

.... (2 marks)

Score / 18

How well did you do?

0–8 correct   Try again
9–17 correct   Getting there
18–23 correct   Good work
24–31 correct   Excellent!

TOTAL SCORE   / 31

For more information on this topic
see pages 68–69 of your Success Guide

CNC IN MANUFACTURING

Choose just one answer, a, b, c or d.

1 CNC stands for:
a) computer number constant
b) control numbering for computers
c) computer numerical control
d) computer national centre (1 mark)

2 Which of the following are not usually operated using CNC?
a) lathes
b) engraving machines
c) marking out tables
d) routing machines (1 mark)

3 Which of the following is not a measurement co-ordinate axis on CNC machines?
a) Q axis   b) Y axis
c) X axis   d) Z axis (1 mark)

4 Which of the following is not widely used as a storage method for CNC programs?
a) smart cards
b) floppy disks
c) CD disks
d) punched tape (1 mark)

5 The route that the cutter makes when it is machining is called the:
a) tool road
b) material road
c) tool path
d) tool route (1 mark)

Score / 5

B Answer all parts of the questions.

1 The diagram shows an incomplete block diagram of a CNC computer system. Complete the diagram by adding the following terms.

memory | keyboard to input program | computer | floppy disk memory | output | input

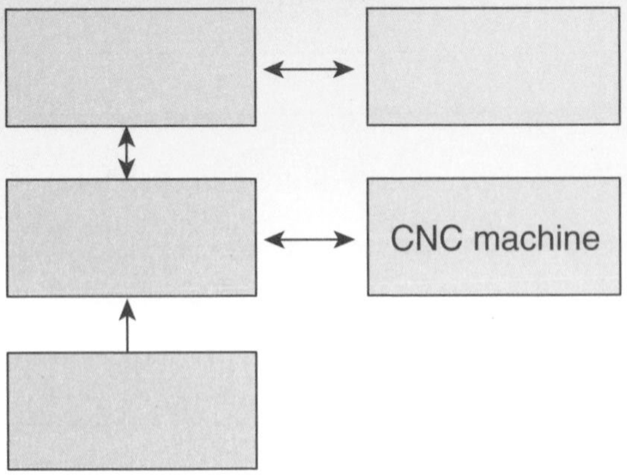

CNC machine

(7 marks)

2 The cutter speed rate is an important factor that needs to be set when programming a CNC machine to machine a particular job.

State three other important machining factors that need to be considered.

....

....

.... (3 marks)

Score / 10

70

C **These are GCSE-style questions. Answer all parts of the questions.**

1 The housings for a wall bookshelf are to be machined using a CNC routing machine. The wood used is MDF.

a) Give three factors you would have to consider before selecting a particular routing machine for the job.

Factor 1 ....

Factor 2 ....

Factor 3 .... (3 marks)

b) Give four advantages of using the CNC router rather than making the housings using traditional hand tools.

....

....

....

.... (4 marks)

c) What safety precautions would have to be taken when machining the material?

....

....

.... (3 marks)

2 CNC engraving machines are often used in school workshops to make labels for design and technology projects.

a) Give four advantages of using such machines.

....

....

....

.... (4 marks)

b) What precautions can be taken to ensure that the small-diameter cutting tools do not break when in use?

....

....

.... (3 marks)

Score   / 17

How well did you do?

0–9 correct   Try again
10–18 correct   Getting there
19–24 correct   Good work
25–32 correct   Excellent!

TOTAL SCORE   **/ 32**

For more information on this topic see pages 70–71 of your Success Guide

TESTING FOR QUALITY

A Choose just one answer, a, b, c or d.

1 A workshop metric micrometer can measure to an accuracy of:
a) 2 mm b) 0.001 mm
c) 0.1 mm d) 1 mm (1 mark)

2 Micrometers that can have automatic readouts are called:
a) external micrometers
b) internal micrometers
c) digital micrometers
d) workshop micrometers (1 mark)

3 A type of accurate calliper is called:
a) a vernier calliper
b) an accurate calliper
c) a G-calliper
d) a slide calliper (1 mark)

4 Spring-joint callipers can be used to measure accuracies of:
a) 3 mm
b) 1 mm
c) 0.25 mm
d) 0.01 mm (1 mark)

5 Which of the following is not a precision measuring tool for metal?
a) internal calliper
b) external micrometer
c) marking gauge
d) external calliper (1 mark)

Score / 5

B Answer all parts of the question.

1 a) The diagram shows the correct way of checking a piece of metal to see if it is square.
Label the diagram showing the datum edge, the engineer's try square, the stock and the work.

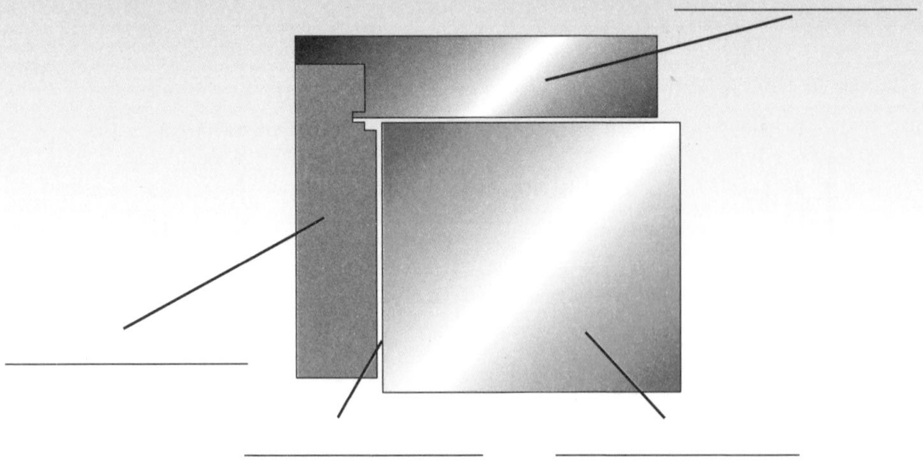

(4 marks)

b) What precautions should be taken to ensure that the tools are accurate when being used?

....

....

....

.... (4 marks)

Score / 8

72

These are GCSE-style questions. Answer all parts of the questions.

1 You have been asked to make the bar and bearing assembly shown for a robotic vehicle.

   a) Indicate three dimensions that would have to be measured accurately when producing the piece.

   (3 marks)

   b) For each measurement give two different tools that you could use.

   ....

   ....

   ....   (3 marks)

   c) For each measurement, state which of the two tools you would select and why you have chosen it.

   ....

   ....

   ....   (3 marks)

2 You have been asked to check some of the measurements before the parts on the metal assembly are fitted together.

   a) What measuring tools would you use to measure dimension A?

   .... (1 mark)

   dimension A
   accuracy — 0.25 mm

   dimension B
   accuracy — 0.002 mm

   b) What measuring tools would you use to measure dimension B?

   .... (1 mark)

   30 mm
   (dimension D)

   c) What measuring tool would you use to measure size C?

   .... (1 mark)

   datum face   70 mm
                  (dimension C)

   d) Describe how you would check whether faces D and C were at right angles to each other.

   ....   (2 marks)

   e) What precautions would you take before taking the measurements to ensure that they were accurate?

   ....   (2 marks)

   Score   / 13

How well did you do?

0–7 correct   Try again
8–13 correct   Getting there
14–19 correct Good work
20–26 correct Excellent!

TOTAL SCORE   **/ 26**

For more information on this topic see pages 72–73 of your Success Guide

TYPES OF PRODUCTION

A Choose just one answer, a, b, c or d.

1 One-off production is often referred to as:
a) batch production
b) job production
c) jig and fixture production
d) in-line production
(1 mark)

2 Motor cars are usually made using:
a) in-line production
b) small batch production
c) concurrent production
d) continuous production
(1 mark)

3 Jigs and fixtures are often used in batch production to:
a) make one-offs
b) speed up the production process
c) allow maintenance to be carried out
d) allow the machine to run without an operation
(1 mark)

4 In-line production normally uses many:
a) graduate operators
b) skilled operators
c) semiskilled operators
d) maintenance operators
(1 mark)

5 The ability to change a machine quickly to make different types of components is called:
a) machine rigidity
b) machine function
c) machine flexibility
d) machine tool ability
(1 mark)

Score   / 5

B Answer all parts of the questions.

1 Decide whether these statements are true or false.

	True	False
a) Job production is used to make large batches of products.	☐	☐
b) Job production tends to use general-purpose machines such as lathes, milling machines and welding equipment.	☐	☐
c) In batch production, batch sizes can vary from small numbers such as 30 or 40 to many thousands of products.	☐	☐
d) Computer-controlled machines are not suitable for batch production.	☐	☐
e) CNC machines are flexible because they can be programmed easily and quickly when different batch sizes are required.	☐	☐

(5 marks)

2 Use these phrases to complete the sentences.

| expensive | breakdowns | mass production | semiskilled operators |

a) In-line production is mainly used for the .... of products such as cars, washing machines and fridges.

b) .... tend to be used during in-line production.

c) In-line production is very .... to set up and thousands of products have to be made to make a profit.

d) In-line production is difficult to plan and .... are costly.   (5 marks)

Score   / 10

C These are GCSE-style questions. Answer all parts of the questions.

1 The diagram below shows a dowelled joint that is to be used as part of a table construction. 300 tables are to be manufactured.

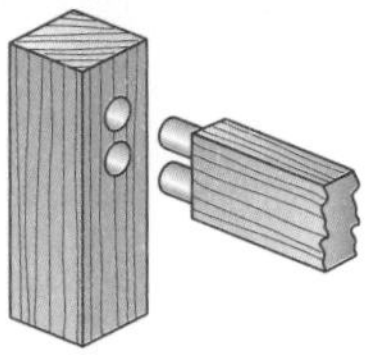

a) Give three advantages of using a jig to carry out the drilling operation.

....

....

.... (3 marks)

b) Explain the advantages of using a computer-controlled machine to drill the holes.

....

....

.... (3 marks)

c) Design a simple jig that could be used to drill the holes on a pillar drill.

(6 marks)

2 **a)** Explain why jigs and fixtures are widely used in batch production.

....

....

....

.... (4 marks)

b) Give two reasons why the introduction of computer-controlled machines has helped reduce the need for jigs and fixtures in the manufacture of products.

....

.... (2 marks)

c) State what is meant by the term 'machine flexibility'.

.... (1 mark)

Score / 19

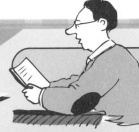

How well did you do?

0–10 correct	Try again
11–19 correct	Getting there
20–27 correct	Good work
28–34 correct	Excellent!

TOTAL SCORE / 34

For more information on this topic see pages 78–79 of your Success Guide

COMMERCIAL SYSTEMS

A

Choose just one answer, a, b, c or d.

1 The term EPOS stands for:
a) engineered positioned operating system
b) electronic point of sale system
c) electronic product operating system
d) engineered product offset system (1 mark)

2 The abbreviation TQM stands for:
a) total quality management
b) traditional quality methods
c) topical quality management
d) training quality methods (1 mark)

3 A group of machines or group of people and machines that works together to produce components is often termed:
a) a milling group
b) a turning group
c) a production cell
d) a in-line conveyor (1 mark)

4 Concurrent manufacture is often used to:
a) reduce electrical and fuel costs
b) increase the overall manufacturing times
c) diagnose electrical costs easily
d) reduce the times between product design and its manufacture (1 mark)

5 Which of the following is not a common term used in production?
a) just in time
b) total quality management
c) concurrent manufacturing
d) standard production methods (1 mark)

Score / 5

B

Answer all parts of the questions.

1 Use the following phrases to complete these sentences.

| respond quickly | weld and spray | team-working cells | batch production |

a) Robots are often used to .... car door panels.

b) The use of production cells can help a company to .... to orders.

c) Groups of people often work in .... to help speed up production.

d) Production cells tend to be used in .... (4 marks)

2 Decide whether these statements are true or false.

	True	False
a) In total quality control, 3 quality checks are only made at the end of the production run.	☐	☐
b) Total quality management relies on everyone in the company being responsible for quality.	☐	☐
c) In total quality management, quality checks are made at regular intervals during the production process.	☐	☐
d) Total quality management helps reduce the number of rejected components.	☐	☐

(4 marks)

Score / 8

76

These are GCSE-style questions. Answer all parts of the questions.

1 **a)** What is meant by the term 'JIT'?

....

....

.... (2 marks)

b) Give three advantages of JIT.

....

....

.... (3 marks)

c) Give two disadvantages of JIT.

....

.... (2 marks)

d) Briefly explain how supermarkets make use of JIT.

....

....

....

....

.... (3 marks)

2 Concurrent manufacturing methods are now used widely in industry to help design and make products.

a) What is meant by the term 'concurrent manufacturing'?

....

....

....

....

.... (3 marks)

b) Give two advantages of concurrent manufacturing.

....

.... (2 marks)

Score   / 15

How well did you do?

0–8 correct   Try again
9–14 correct   Getting there
15–22 correct   Good work
23–28 correct   Excellent!

TOTAL SCORE   / 28

For more information on this topic
see pages 80–81 of your Success Guide

BATCH PRODUCTION

A

Choose just one answer, a, b, c or d.

1 **A jig is normally used for:**
a) forging   b) die casting
c) drilling   d) extrusion   (1 mark)

2 **A jig is a work-holding device that:**
a) also guides the tool during machining
b) can only be made from wood
c) is not widely used in batch
d) is only used for lathe turning operations
                                          (1 mark)

3 **Many modern machines are computer-controlled and they can:**
a) replace the need for jigs and fixtures
b) make the equipment more complicated
c) reduce the accuracy of the product
d) work with wood, metals and plastics
                                          (1 mark)

4 **An example of a direct cost is:**
a) the wages for office staff
b) general lighting costs
c) cost of materials per product
d) factory rates   (1 mark)

5 **A fixture is a work-holding device that is:**
a) not clamped to the table
b) clamped to the table
c) placed in the drill chuck
d) made solely for plastics materials   (1 mark)

Score   / 5

B

Answer all parts of the questions.

1 Use these terms to complete the following sentences.

| clamped | guides | milling | drilling |

a) A jig is a device which locates and holds the workpiece in place and also .... the tool.

b) A fixture is a work-holding device that is .... to the table.

c) Jigs are normally used for .... and reaming.

d) Fixtures tend to be used for .... , turning and grinding.

                                          (4 marks)

2 Give four factors that should be considered when designing a simple jig.

Factor 1 ....

....

Factor 2 ....

....

Factor 3 ....

....

Factor 4 ....

....
                                          (4 marks)

Score   / 8

C

These are GCSE-style questions. Answer all parts of the questions.

1 The peg game shown is to be made in a batch of 500 out of wood. The holes can be made using either a CNC drilling machine or a non-CNC drilling machine.

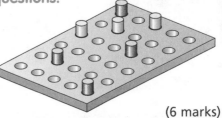

a) In the table below make a list of the likely costs for each production method.

(6 marks)

CNC Costs	Jigs and Fixtures Costs

b) Give three reasons why jigs are used in schools and industry for drilling operations.

....

....

.... (3 marks)

c) What is a Gantt chart?

.... (1 mark)

2 You have been asked by a company to make a list of the likely costs of making 10 000 components on a milling machine.

a) Why would it be a good idea to use a fixture for the task?

....

....

....

.... (5 marks)

b) Make a list of the costs of making the product that you would consider.

....

....

....

.... (6 marks)

c) Why might it be unwise to use a fixture if only one product was required?

....

.... (2 marks)

Score   / 23

How well did you do?

0–12 correct   Try again
13–21 correct   Getting there
22–29 correct   Good work
30–36 correct   Excellent!

TOTAL SCORE   / 36

For more information on this topic see pages 82–83 of your Success Guide

USE OF STANDARD COMPONENTS

A

Choose just one answer, a, b, c or d.

1 The term BS stands for:
a) Birmingham Standard
b) Business Standard
c) British Standard
d) Business Structure   (1 mark)

2 An M3 screw thread will have a diameter of:
a) 3 inches
b) 3 cm
c) 3 mm
d) 0.3 mm   (1 mark)

3 Components such as nuts and bolts are examples of:
a) standard components
b) non-flexible components
c) strategic components
d) non-standard components   (1 mark)

4 Standard components are normally bought in by a company to:
a) expand the company
b) make the product more complicated
c) reduce overall costs
d) create more jobs   (1 mark)

5 Modern factories generally try to order standard parts:
a) just in time for manufacture
b) 12 months before the stock needs to be used
c) so that very large stocks can be held all at once
d) so that all the parts are bought in at once
                                        (1 mark)

Score   / 5

B

Answer all parts of the questions.

1 Give three reasons why standard parts are bought in from suppliers.

....

....

....   (3 marks)

2 a) Give four examples of standard components.

....

....

....

....   (4 marks)

b) Give two examples where each might be used.

....

....

....

....

....

....   (4 marks)

Score   / 11

C **These are GCSE-style questions. Answer all parts of the questions.**

1 The diagram below shows a central axle assembly
for the spindle of a toy fairground ride.

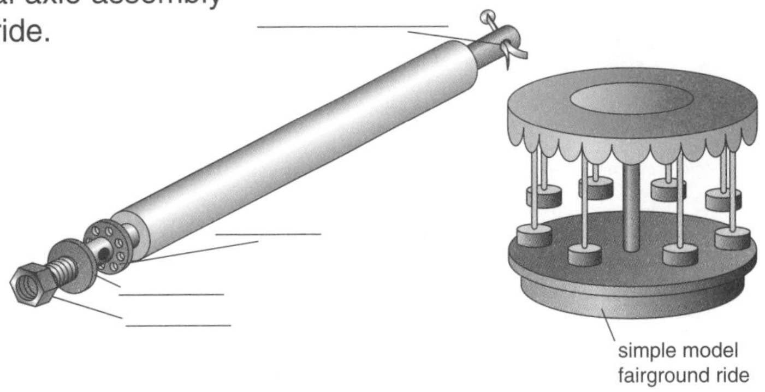

simple model
fairground ride

a) Label the sketch naming the types of standard parts shown. (3 marks)

b) How would you obtain information about the standard parts?

....

.... (2 marks)

c) What factors would you consider before purchasing the parts?

....

....

.... (3 marks)

2 Manufacturers making bicycles buy in many types of standard
components from other suppliers.

a) Name three types of standard components they could buy in from the suppliers.

....

....

.... (3 marks)

b) Give three advantages of buying in standard components.

....

....

.... (3 marks)

c) Give one reason why the bicycle manufacturer might use a just-in-time system
when buying in the components.

.... (1 mark)

Score   / 15

How well did you do?

0–6 correct   Try again
7–16 correct   Getting there
17–24 correct   Good work
25–31 correct   Excellent!

TOTAL SCORE   / 31

For more information on this topic
see pages 84–85 of your Success Guide

USE OF CAD/CAM IN INDUSTRY

A Choose just one answer, a, b, c or d.

1 The term CAD is an abbreviation for:
a) computer accelerated design
b) computer aided development
c) component accelerated development
d) computer aided design   (1 mark)

2 The term CNC stands for:
a) computer national centre
b) computer navigating console
c) computer numerical control
d) computer numbering criterion   (1 mark)

3 Programmes for CNC are often stored on:
a) smart cards   c) bit cards
b) business cards   d) byte cards (1 mark)

4 An industry robot is a device that:
a) can be reprogrammed for different aspects
b) cannot be reprogrammed once they are set up
c) never needs maintenance when running
d) cannot be used in hazardous conditions
                                        (1 mark)

5 Which of the following operations is not usually carried out using robots?
a) designing products
b) paint spraying
c) spot welding
d) component handling   (1 mark)

Score   / 5

B Answer all parts of the questions.

1 Complete the crossword that has questions linked to CAD/CAM operations.

Across
1. Abbreviation for computer numerical control.
2. How information is sent to the memory from a floppy disk.
3. What the 'T' stands for in JIT.
4. What the 'D' stands for in CAD.

Down
1. Links with CAM.
2. Data is often stored on these.
3. Common pieces of equipment controlled by computers.
4. A process often carried out by robots.

(8 marks)

2 Give three advantages of using CAD packages in the design of products.

....
....
....
(3 marks)

3 Choose one of these phrases to complete each of the sentences.

| computer-controlled | gripping device | welding | new sequence |

a) Industrial robots are .... devices that can be reprogrammed.

b) A robot can be reprogrammed with a .... of movements and can be easily adapted for different operations.

c) Robots usually have interchangeable ....

d) A typical use of a robot is for ....
(4 marks)

Score   / 15

C **These are GCSE-style questions. Answer all parts of the questions.**

1 A number of shields for a design and technology competition are to be designed and made with the aid of CAD/CAM.

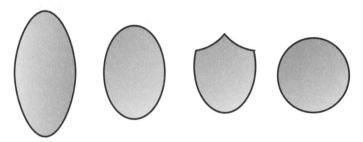

a) Explain how CAD/CAM could be used to manufacture the shields.

....

....

....

.... (4 marks)

b) Explain how CAD/CAM could reduce the time between designing and making.

....

....

.... (3 marks)

2 CAD/CAM systems are widely used for the design and manufacture of products in schools and industry.

a) What is meant by the term 'CAD solid modelling'?

....

.... (2 marks)

b) Give three advantages of using CAM for making products.

....

....

.... (3 marks)

c) Give two ways in which programs may be saved when using CAM machines.

....

.... (2 marks)

Score   / 14

How well did you do?

0–10 correct   Try again
11–19 correct   Getting there
20–27 correct   Good work
28–34 correct   Excellent!

TOTAL SCORE   / 34

For more information on this topic see pages 86–87 of your Success Guide

COMPUTER INTEGRATED SYSTEMS

A

Choose just one answer, a, b, c or d.

1 CIM stands for:
a) computer installed system
b) control integration system
c) computer integrated system
d) computer integrated manufacture (1 mark)

2 Which of the following is not normally regarded as part of a CIM system?
a) computer aided design
b) non-automatic lathes
c) computer operated machinery
d) material handling systems (1 mark)

3 Many CIM systems have a:
a) centralised computer
b) non-centralised computer
c) non-computerised stock system
d) manual machine (1 mark)

4 CIM systems usually:
a) are cheap to install
b) are very expensive to install
c) work using punch cards
d) are not found in industry (1 mark)

5 CIM systems are very often used with:
a) a small company's stock control
b) small computer systems
c) manual production control systems
d) just-in-time control systems (1 mark)

Score / 5

B

Answer all parts of the questions.

Decide whether these statements are true or false.

		True	False
1	CIM systems are cheap to install.	☐	☐
2	CIM systems tend to be installed in large organisations such as aerospace companies.	☐	☐
3	CIM systems are very integrated where a powerful computer controls production.	☐	☐
4	CIM is never used for stock control.	☐	☐
5	CAD is usually part of a CIM system.	☐	☐
6	CIM effectively networks a company together.	☐	☐

(6 marks)

Score / 6

C **These are GCSE-style questions. Answer all parts of the questions.**

1 CIM systems are widely used to help produce aircraft like the one shown in the diagram.

a) What is meant by the term 'CIM'?

.... (1 mark)

b) Give three advantages of using a CIM system in a factory.

....

....

.... (3 marks)

c) Give three disadvantages of using the CIM system.

....

....

.... (3 marks)

2 Many companies now make use of computer integrated manufacturing (CIM) systems to help manufacture their products.

a) List three company areas or tasks that might be linked together by a central CIM computer.

....

....

.... (3 marks)

b) Give two reasons why many companies may not have CIM systems.

....

.... (2 marks)

c) Sketch a block diagram showing how the various parts of a company might be integrated by a CIM system.

(3 marks)

Score   / 15

How well did you do?

0–6 correct   Try again
7–12 correct   Getting there
13–20 correct   Good work
21–26 correct   Excellent!

TOTAL SCORE   **/ 26**

For more information on this topic
see pages 88–89 of your Success Guide

CONTROLLING THE QUALITY

A

Choose just one answer, a, b, c or d.

1 TQM stands for:
a) total quantitative methods
b) traditional quality management
c) total quality management
d) tool quality methods   (1 mark)

2 Which of the following is not a type of measurement gauge?
a) plug gauge
b) gap gauge
c) taper plug gauge
d) wooden gauge   (1 mark)

3 Faulty goods are called:
a) rejects   b) products
c) failjects   d) mis-products   (1 mark)

4 An international quality standard is:
a) BS 2000
b) BS 500
c) ISO 9000
d) ISO 999   (1 mark)

5 A graph for checking the quality of a manufacturing process is called a:
a) control chart
b) pie chart
c) pictograph
d) size chart   (1 mark)

Score   / 5

B

Answer all parts of the question.

1 a) Explain what is meant by 100% inspection.

....

....

....

....   (2 marks)

b) Explain the difference between a variable and an attribute when considering the quality of a product.

....

....

....

....   (2 marks)

c) Explain what is meant by tolerance.

....

....

....

....

....

....   (3 marks)

Score   / 7

These are GCSE-style questions. Answer all parts of the questions.

1 a) With the aid of sketches describe the difference between an interference fit
and a clearance fit.

(3 marks)

b) Give one example where each type of fit might be used.

....

.... (2 marks)

c) Sketch a gap gauge identifying the main parts.

(3 marks)

2 The diagram shows the dimensions of a round shaft
that needs to revolve in the hole in the plate.

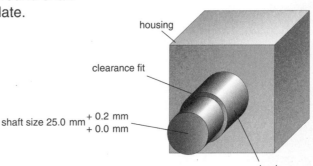

housing

clearance fit

shaft size 25.0 mm $^{+\,0.2\ mm}_{+\,0.0\ mm}$

bush

a) What is the upper limit of the shaft size? .... (1 mark)

b) What is the lower limit of the shaft size? .... (1 mark)

c) What is meant by the term 'tolerance'? .... (1 mark)

d) Determine the tolerance for the shaft. .... (2 marks)

e) What would happen if the hole was the same size as the shaft?

.... (1 mark)

f) What sort of gauge could be used to check the size of the shaft if many were
being manufactured?

.... (2 marks)

Score   / 16

How well did you do?

0–8 correct   Try again
9–14 correct   Getting there
15–22 correct Good work
23–28 correct Excellent!

TOTAL SCORE   / 28

For more information on this topic
see pages 90–91 of your Success Guide

MIXED GCSE-STYLE QUESTIONS

1 A menu holder as shown in the diagram is to be made from 4 mm plastic sheet.

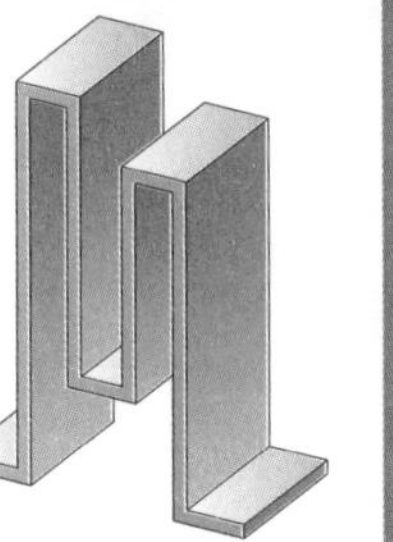

a) What type of plastic could be used?

.... (1 mark)

b) Explain how you would make the holder from the plastic sheet stage.

....

....

.... (3 marks)

c) If a large batch of holders were to be made, how could this be achieved in practice?

....

.... (3 marks)

2 This table has to be assembled from a flat-pack kit.

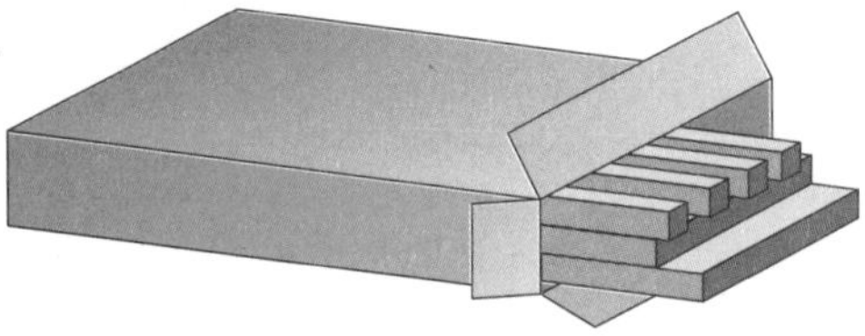

a) State two advantages that flat-pack furniture provides for the customers.

....

.... (2 marks)

b) Give two advantages to the manufacturer.

....

.... (3 marks)

c) Draw a type of knock-down fitting that might be used to join the furniture together.

(3 marks)

3 A manufacturer needs to produce an airline flight tray.

    a) State three factors that you would need to find out before you started the design.

    ....

    ....

    ....   (3 marks)

    b) List four factors that you would put into the specification.

    ....

    ....

    ....

    ....   (4 marks)

    c) What manufacturing issue would you consider before deciding on the final design?

    ....   (1 mark)

4 Both wooden and plastic conservatory tables are available in a local shop.

    a) State two reasons why you might choose the plastic table.

    ....

    ....   (2 marks)

    b) State two reasons why you might choose the wooden table.

    ....

    ....   (2 marks)

    c) Briefly discuss any environmental issues you would consider before purchasing the chair of your choice.

    ....

    ....

    ....   (3 marks)

5 10 000 plastic toy animals are to be manufactured as a promotion for a fast food chain.

    a) Name a type of plastic that would be suitable.

    ....   (1 mark)

    b) Name a process that would be suitable for making the toy animals.

    ....   (2 marks)

    c) Describe the process you have chosen and give three reasons why it is suitable for the manufacture.

    ....

    ....

    ....

    ....   (4 marks)

d) What safety precautions would the fast food chain have to consider before putting the toys on the market?

....

....

....

.... (2 marks)

6 a) What is meant by the term 'batch production'?

....

.... (2 marks)

b) With the aid of sketches describe how jigs are used in batch production situations.

(4 marks)

7 a) What is meant by the term 'TQM'?

....

.... (1 marks)

b) Explain how TQM operates in a company and how it can improve the products being made.

....

....

....

....

.... (3 marks)

8 A jewellery pendant is to be made in large numbers from sheet brass.

a) Give three reasons why it would be better to press the part out rather than machining.

....

....

.... (3 marks)

b) Once the part has been made, how could it be protected against tarnishing?

.... (1 mark)

c) What safety factors would you have to consider when designing the piece of jewellery?

....

.... (2 marks)

9 The small aluminium alloy component shown is to be made using a casting process. 15 000 components have to be made.

a) What casting method would you use to produce the parts?

.... (1 mark)

b) Describe the process you have chosen.

....

....

.... (3 marks)

c) Give three advantages of using this method rather than using other methods.

....

....

.... (3 marks)

10 A series of 50 mm holes has to be drilled as part of a design in a beech cabinet.

a) State whether the timber is a hardwood or softwood.

.... (1 mark)

b) Name the tool that you would use.

.... (2 marks)

c) Describe how you would carry out the operation on a pillar drilling machine.

....

....

....

.... (3 marks)

11 A sand-cast lamp base has been made in a school workshop.

The lamp stem has to be secured into the base using a screw thread.

a) Explain how the top of the base could be marked out ready for producing the internal screw thread.

....

....

.... (3 marks)

b) Explain how the internal thread can be made.

....

....

.... (3 marks)

c) What tool would be used to make the external thread on the lamp stem?

.... (1 mark)

12 A small jewellery box is to be made from wood.

    a) What type of wood could be used to make the box?

.... (1 mark)

    b) What type of joints could be used to make the box?

.... (2 marks)

    c) What tools would be used to make the joints you have named in **b)**?

....

.... (2 marks)

    d) What finishing processes could be used to make the box?

....

.... (1 mark)

13 A mould to make pewter badges is to be made using a CNC routing machine.
The material for the mould is MDF.

    a) What does MDF stand for?

.... (1 mark)

    b) Give four advantages of using a CNC machine rather than making the mould by hand.

....

....

....

.... (4 marks)

    c) Name a process that could be used to manufacture large batches of aluminium badges
       if they were to be made in industry.

.... (2 marks)

14 You have been asked to make ten plant labels for a local parks garden.

    a) State three properties that the material would require.

....

....

.... (3 marks)

b) Name a type of plastic that might be suitable for the label.

.... (1 mark)

c) Describe how you could make the labels in your school workshop.

....

....

.... (3 marks)

15 A model fairground ride is to be driven by a small motor.

a) Name three types of possible belt drive sections that could be used.

....

....

.... (3 marks)

b) Describe how the belt could be adjusted to prevent too much slippage when the ride was in operation.

....

.... (1 mark)

c) Give two other ways of transmitting motion.

.... (2 marks)

16 A piece of armour needs to be made for a school play. It has been decided to make the product using a glass reinforced plastics (fibre glass composite).

a) Describe the method you would use to make the piece of armour.

....

....

....

.... (4 marks)

b) Give three safety precautions that would have to be observed when making it.

....

....

.... (3 marks)

c) Explain why this method might be better than making the armour out of sheet metal.

....

....

.... (3 marks)

GCSE Mixed Questions - Answers

1 **a)** Perspex.

   b) Mark out plastic sheet using scriber to mark lines which need to be cut and felt-tipped pen for other lines. Cut to size. Use strip heater to heat where plastic needs to be bent. Bend to shape.

   c) Batch production method – or injection moulding if sheet was not used.

2 **a)** Easy to transport, relatively cheap.

   b) Cheap to manufacture, easy to store.

   c)

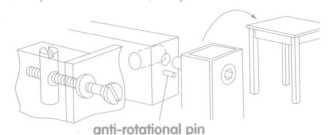

anti-rotational pin

3 **a)** Answers include: how product will be used, temperature ranges, weight of product, maximum/minimum dimensions, target cost, safety specifications, colour, shape, ergonomic factors, manufacturing specifications.

   b) Answers include: colour, shape and size, ergonomic factors, manufacturing specifications.

   c) Most cost-effective method of production, target delivery date.

4 **a)** Easy to clean, light.

   b) Appearance, hard-wearing.

   c) Made from renewable resources.

5 **a)** Polystyrene.

   b) Injection moulding.

   c) Plastics are fed from hopper. Plastics heated and fed through screw, heated plastic forced into split mould, mould cooled by water, mould opened and toy ejected automatically. Suitable for long production run, product can be coloured, made quickly with little finishing, relatively cheap once equipment has been bought.

   d) Size of toy conforms to standards of safety for small children, no sharp edges.

6 **a)** Batch production involves producing specified number of identical products in groups.

   b) When large numbers of identical components are made, time-consuming to measure and mark off each component individually before manufacture. Jigs and fixtures used to speed up process by locating piece quickly and clamp into place so measuring and marking does not need to be done. Answer should include sketches.

7 **a)** TQM is total quality management.

   b) TQM can improve quality of processes and procedures and products because quality systems are introduced at every stage of production and within organisation. TQM seeks to make product right first time every time.

8 **a)** Answers could include: less waste material, a cheaper option and consistent accuracy for all the pendants.

   b) Protect against tarnishing using lacquer.

   c) Ensure no sharp edges.

9 **a)** Sand casting.

b) Sand is moulded by hand or machine around wooden or metal pattern. This is withdrawn leaving cavity of required shape in mould. Most moulds made in two halves to aid mould-making process. Molten metal poured into runner. Risers allow gas and air to escape during casting. Size and shape of pattern must take into account shrinkage that will occur during solidification. Finished castings are fettled to remove excess metal.

c) Answers include: low-cost method of producing general castings, cost-effective for low production volumes, pattern can be re-used.

10 **a)** Hardwood.

b) Hand drill or pillar drill (hole saw).

c) Mark off the position for the hole. Select the correct size hole saw. Clamp wood in vice or use G-clamps to secure wood. Select correct speeds for drilling operations. Drill wood with pilot hole and then drill full size holes. Clean up with glass paper.

11 **a)** Marking blue is applied to the surface so that scriber lines are visible. Dividers are used to mark out the circle for the thread.

b) A tap is used to cut the hole. A cutting paste is used to aid the operation.

c) The external thread would be made using dies.

12 **a)** The box could be made from scots pine or spruce.

b) The joints could be finger joints.

c) The finger joints would be made using tenon saws and bevel-edged chisels.

d) The box could be cleaned using glass paper and then varnished or stained.

13 **a)** MDF is medium-density fibreboard.

b) CNC routers give an accurate finish, can be programmed to machine intricate shapes, speed up production process and are fully enclosed in a cabinet which has dust extraction.

c) Aluminium badges could be made using investment casting.

14 **a)** Good resistance to moisture, light and stiff.

b) Polystyrene.

c) Measure and mark shape out of plastics using rule, engineer's try square and chinagraph pencil. Cut out shape with a junior hacksaw, hacksaw or coping saw. File it to shape. Clean up edge with wet and dry paper.

15 **a)** round belt, vee belt, flat belt

b) A screw thread could be used as a tensioning device. The thread could have a bolt head so that a spanner can be used to make adjustments.

c) gear drives, cams, lever mechanisms

16 **a)** Hand lay up method with glass reinforced plastics. Wooden mould made to the shape of the hull. Mould smoothed down to ensure a good finish. Release agent brushed over the mould. Layer of plastic resin brushed over release agent and mould. Fibre glass to form the next layer. This is rolled into the matrix plastics. Layer of plastics and fibre glass built up to the required depth.

b) wear gloves, face masks and work in a well ventilated room

c) Cheaper and easier method to make small batches than by metal pressing. Less energy is used and the hulls can be made up by hand rather than investing in expensive machinery.

How well did you do?

0–30	Try again
31–60	Getting there
61–90	Good work
91–110	Excellent!